Math Is a Verb

Activities and Lessons from Cultures Around the World

Jim Barta

Bemidji State University
Bemidji, Minnesota

Ron Eglash

Rensselaer Polytechnic Institute
Troy, New York

Cathy Barkley

Colorado Mesa University
Grand Junction, Colorado

More resources available online
www.nctm.org/more4u
Access code: MVB14326

NCTM® | NATIONAL COUNCIL OF TEACHERS OF MATHEMATICS

Copyright © 2014 by
The National Council of Teachers of Mathematics, Inc.
1906 Association Drive, Reston, VA 20191-1502
(703) 620-9840; (800) 235-7566; www.nctm.org
All rights reserved

Library of Congress Cataloging-in-Publication Data

Barta, James, 1955–
  Math is a verb: Activities and lessons from cultures around the world / James Barta, Ron
Eglash, Cathy Barkley.
      pages cm
  ISBN 978-0-87353-707-0
  1. Ethnomathematics. 2. Mathematics—Social aspects. I. Eglash, Ron, 1958– author. II.
Barkley, Cathy A. (Cathy Anne), 1951– author. III. Title.
  GN476.15.B37 2013
  510.89--dc23
                              2013036514

The National Council of Teachers of Mathematics is the public voice of mathematics education,
supporting teachers to ensure equitable mathematics learning of the highest quality for all
students through vision, leadership, professional development, and research.

Printed in the United States of America

CONTENTS

PREFACE

"Mathematics is a verb! In Ute we do not have just one word to describe mathematics—rather, we name it as we use it. When we count, build, design, cook, hunt, or fish, we are doing mathematics."

—Fabian Jenks, a Northern Ute elder from Fort Duchesne, Utah

For most people, the word *mathematics* is a noun. But as the above quote (Barta and Shockey 2006) shows, not everyone would agree. For many people in many different cultures, mathematics is not simply something they learn in school. It is instead something they *do* as an intrinsic part of their everyday lives.

Math Is a Verb: Activities and Lessons from Cultures Around the World is a guide for teachers who would like to enhance their mathematics instruction by integrating it with examples and activities of cultures throughout the world. This book provides culturally situated examples, each linked to Common Core objectives, that show how mathematics is so much more than an arbitrary story problem residing in a text, or an exercise in a worksheet with little or no context. Mathematics is a process shaped and influenced by its use and by the culture of those using it. In many parts of the world, mathematics is named by how people use it; it is through its application that we see how culture influences mathematics and, reciprocally, how mathematics affects culture.

Traditionally, mathematics has been described as a universal language, and to a degree this is true. However, it may be more useful to think of mathematics as a language composed of a variety of dialects we use as we think, communicate, and evaluate data to solve the unique problems faced in each of our communities. Of course, people in every community add, subtract, multiply, and divide, but exactly *how* we do this varies broadly because of the influence of culture on naming, thinking, and doing.

When we embrace a more multicultural understanding of mathematics, we see how the mathematics of today has evolved from many cultures' contributions from across the planet and throughout time. Mathematics is not a subject that is fixed, rigid, and fully developed; it is instead a process that in many ways continues to evolve and that possesses life, animation, and applicability as it remains responsive to those who name it and use it. This perspective alone suggests that children can learn mathematics more effectively if they are taught in ways that provide relevance and meaning, while also respecting and validating the communities and cultures the children represent.

In this book, we have provided teachers with representative mathematical examples from a variety of cultural communities throughout the world, making a particular effort to include cultures not typically seen in other multicultural mathematics books. The mathematical connections made here are to groups at varying socioeconomic levels, as well as ones from both industrialized and nonindustrialized countries, and from both indigenous and nonindigenous societies. We do this to encourage teachers to further investigate their own understanding of culture and its influence on how they teach an increasingly diverse student population.

Our goal is not merely to ensure that students realize the global nature of mathematics. We also hope that more students in our increasingly diverse classrooms will become inspired when they see their own culture and mathematical heritage showcased. We realize that one book can barely scratch the surface of culturally applied mathematical examples from around the world. While we consider our examples distinctively unique, they represent only a smattering of the countless rich and varied examples of peoples across the planet knowing, doing, and using mathematics. We hope that as teachers study how others learn and apply mathematics within the local contexts and cultures described in this book, they will realize that they too can create personalized math lessons specifically developed for those they teach.

Acknowledgments

A montage of mathematical connections to cultures around the world such as this one necessarily requires a host of contributors. It would have been virtually impossible to write a book using examples and activities of cultures from throughout the world without the contributions of numerous consultants, guides, and collaborators. In naming anyone, we run the risk of unintentionally omitting others, and we offer a sincere apology in advance for anyone accidentally not included here.

We extend heartfelt thanks to the following for their individual and collective contributions: Tod Shockey, Audrey Grace Bennett, Lucas Sánchez, Daniel Clark Orey, Milton Rosa, Clayton Long, Enoch Bulley, Reiner Kreitner, Dan Lyles, Bill Babbitt, Gabriel Boakye, Barbara Dougherty, Madhuri Bapat, Vessela Ilieva, Donka Chardakova, Richard Sgarlotti, Chadd McGlone, Richard Bonsu, Eric Kwarteng, and Jacob Barta. To our cultural consultants, we appreciate the trust you have shown us by sharing cultural knowledge, values, and traditions that should always be treated with the utmost dignity and respect in the classroom. Each of you in your own way has helped paint the world with mathematics, and you have enabled others to view and appreciate its beauty and to deepen their understanding of the role and power of mathematics in societies around the world.

INTRODUCTION
The Crossroads of Mathematics and Culture

Imagine that you are a young African American student just getting to a class in arts or social studies. In today's lesson you might get to learn about African culture, sculpt with clay, or watch a video on the Underground Railroad. Now imagine you are that same student heading to math class. Will today's lesson on how to find the least common multiple and the greatest common factor hold your interest just as much?

We all know the criticism: Students should be as interested in math as they are in their other school subjects, so if they are not, the fault lies with them. But what if that thinking is wrong? What if there are other ways to teach mathematics to students—ways that turn it into a bridge to their own heritage culture? A ticket to far-off, fascinating places? Or a new medium for sculpting fantastic shapes and for expressing personal and social ideas?

Traditionally, mathematics has been considered a subject one studied in school to learn and practice procedures using numbers and symbols written as algorithms. Mathematics is too often presented as a set of static, unchanging rules developed by ancient people with no connection to current problem solving. In this book, we wish to challenge and expand this perception by suggesting that a far greater number of "mathematicians" use and apply mathematical principles every day.

Some researchers suggest that many students, and in particular many minority students, believe that mathematics has been developed and is owned by a community they are not a part of (Barta, Cuch, and Exton 2012). Gaps in achievement scores have been tied to this disconnect between students in certain communities and how they view and experience what they consider to be another group's mathematics. Rather than focusing on gaps in achievement, we suggest a part of the problem is related to gaps in opportunities for all students to learn mathematics in ways they see as relevant to their identities and communities. While few like to admit it, some teachers, parents, and students still hold to the pervasive misconception that mathematical potential is somehow related to one's genetic background! This belief has no merit, of course, yet what has changed in the way we teach mathematics that will allow a greater inclusion and connection to an increasingly diverse student cultural population? Across the globe, people who would never be considered mathematicians are engaged with mathematical activities in the work they complete, the artifacts they construct, or the objects they design. Mathematics is best understood as we experience its application within the cultures and contexts in which it is applied. Everyone in the world is similar in that we all have a spoken language through which we communicate thoughts and ideas. Within this similarity, however, are unique differences shaped and defined by culture and communicated through the diverse vocabulary, syntax, and semantics of each language. Mathematics too is a language comprised of many dialects—dialects that denote diverse communities using mathematics.

A Brief History of Using Culture in Mathematics Instruction

Over time, different approaches and degrees of including culture(s) in the mathematics classroom have prevailed. Here, we will briefly summarize three historic stages of using culture in mathematics teaching as we have experienced them. The stages are *traditional, multicultural,* and *culturally responsive.* It is important for mathematics educators to know of these stages and to consider their implications on teaching and learning.

Several decades ago, the Roman numeral system was one of the few examples of culture included in mathematics instruction. The use of culture in this period can be described as "traditional," because teachers made few, if any, cultural connections as they taught the Roman numeral system. Numbers were merely written as part of exercises to be practiced, often without any story or contextual meaning. Story problems provided a very generalized context describing Eurocentric situations and expectations. Students learned that culture was not a part of mathematics, and even when mathematics was contextualized in a story or situation, that context represented the majority culture.

Authors writing textbooks eventually began to add a multicultural element to the instruction, as they occasionally included examples of diverse cultures demonstrating mathematical concepts and procedures. Certainly this multicultural stage was a step forward from the Roman numeral days, but all too often these inclusions were historical examples, which seldom included living representatives. Mathematics, even when considered from a cultural perspective, was too often presented as something that was practiced in the past by people no longer living.

We will share several historical examples of cultural mathematics in this book, but a far greater portion of our work involves the integration of culturally responsive mathematics instruction. We define culturally responsive mathematics—this third stage in the use of culture within mathematics teaching—as the way that mathematics influences a culture and, conversely, the way that culture shapes the mathematical application being used. The reciprocal interaction of mathematics and culture demands a powerful revision of those previous instructional periods of the traditional and multicultural. Rather than vaguely connected or historical in emphasis, culturally responsive mathematics instruction is contemporary and active.

The available opportunities for connecting mathematics and cultures are as varied as the people living on our planet. When teachers educate from such a perspective, they help their students to see that mathematics is far more than an isolated subject. The study instead becomes a way to understand the role mathematics plays in shaping culture and the ways that culture guides and responds to the use of mathematics in the lives of those who use it. Such inclusivity allows all students the opportunity to celebrate the mathematical heritage of their people(s) as they gain deeper insights into mathematical concepts and principles.

Our Central Themes

Teachers are usually excited to find new activities they can use with their students, and students certainly enjoy instructional variety and like to be meaningfully and actively engaged. We believe our global examples of engagement with mathematics will fulfill the needs of both teachers and students. To ensure that teachers who use the materials in this book comprehend key aspects of this instruction, we have provided them with a new way of approaching mathematics with their students within an ethnomathematical lens. *Ethnomathematics* can be defined as the study of the relationships between mathematics and cultures (D'Ambrosio 2001).

By incorporating this study, teachers and students alike can experience mathematics in new and novel ways. Teachers who understand the key components of these materials will better realize the beauty of this integration and its complexity. They can then help their students develop a new relationship to mathematics. Rather than study mathematics from the viewpoint of a spectator, students can participate in mathematical processes that become even more relevant and intriguing when curricular boundaries between mathematics, its applications, and cultures become blurred or nonexistent.

This book emphasizes three specific themes: (1) *authentic application,* (2) *life in numbers,* and (3) *intentional intelligence and use.* Of these three, authentic application may be the most self-evident. As the term implies, it is the active use of mathematics within a situation or context to solve a problem. Alan Bishop, noted ethnomathematician, has suggested that people across the world and throughout time have used mathematics to count, measure, design, locate, explain, and play (Bishop 1988). These six universal actions can be used to investigate the math in what people do, how they live, what they build, and where they live. These universals make apparent the mathematics of an activity, object, or action as the reciprocal interaction of mathematics and the culture. Mathematics becomes best understood by how it is used. Similar activities are practiced by many diverse cultures, and so we are witness to a countless variety of possible solutions to a problem. Divergent thinking, along with a growing understanding of how we can do the same things differently and still succeed, provides a palatable example to expand notions of respect, tolerance, and cultural understanding. As teachers better understand the benefits of employing an ethnomathematical perspective in their teaching, issues surrounding social justice can be explored. Mathematics that is taught from a traditional perspective excludes many cultures that shared in the worldwide discovery and application of mathematics. As mathematics and culture come to be seen as integral components of one another, issues of equity can be examined and greater inclusivity can result.

The concept of *life in numbers* describes a relationship between the action, personality, and animation of numbers with the people using them in a given situation. The traditional view of mathematics as a study with no cultural component divorced the student from the idea that one could interact with the numbers and develop a relationship with them. An example may help to best illustrate this idea. Elmer Ghostkeeper, a mathematics consultant from Alberta, Canada, was asked why he thought a number of First Nations/American Indian students struggled with mathematics. Elmer, who is himself Métis (First Nation), stated, "Some of our children struggle with mathematics because the numbers do not dance!" (Barta, Jetté, and Wiseman 2003).

Similar to a dance, there exist a number of unique steps peculiar to specific cultures and responsive to the instruments and music that accompany them. As students develop their own relationships and understanding with mathematics resulting from relevant, deep, and personal interactions, they learn to dance with the numbers. When viewed in such a light, numbers do tell stories and models convey meanings. Mathematizing, or the act of mathematical thinking or doing, results from the interaction between the mathematician and the object or activity with which they participate.

Intentional intelligence and use is our last theme, and it serves to debunk the oft-presented notion that people in society who employ informal applications of mathematics (that is, out-of-school applications of mathematical principles and concepts) are seldom aware of what they are doing or why they use a particular concept or strategy. We instead explain such intentionality as the purposeful application of mathematical intelligence to challenge an issue or solve a problem. Such informal applications show the conscious use of one's intelligence to seek a solution, complete a real-life task, or solve a problem in the community. Intentionality requires that teachers become more sophisticated in the examples they use when illustrating culture in the mathematics classroom. Occasionally a "tourist approach" has been used in mathematics classrooms. As children study some far-away country, word problems describe the food, object, or clothes of the day—i.e., *Jaime has three sombreros and Louisa has two more. How many sombreros do they have together at the fiesta?* It is not impossible for a sombrero or a fiesta to provide numerous connections to study mathematics while illustrating a culture. However, when used as in the above example, the object or activity presented adds little to our understanding of either mathematics or the culture. We could have selected virtually any two objects in our attempt to teach children the concept. Intentionality provides us with a better understanding of how the person using the mathematics was thinking of it, and we begin to develop a more accurate understanding of the cultural traditions, values, and meanings inherent in the object or activity.

The Journey Ahead

This book encompasses eleven world cultures and applications of mathematics presented through classroom activities. We provide an activity specific to each culture for the grade bands of kindergarten–grade 3, grades 4–8, and grades 9–12. Each chapter is framed around an artifact, game, or activity, with an emphasis on the rich cultural knowledge of its use and meaning within its culture, as well as a focus on the intentional use of the mathematics or concepts embedded in its production or deployment. Our hands-on, inquiry-based activities also often include technology-infused, web-based learning designed to provide a variety of instructional applications for a broad range of students.

The first chapter, **Cornrow Hair Braiding,** considers an intersection of mathematics and culture found in communities in Africa, Jamaica, and the United States. Using web-based software, students will learn skills involving counting, collecting and organizing data, patterns, multiplication, Cartesian coordinates, geometric transformations and sequence, and iteration as they create their own cornrow designs and investigate and apply the mathematics they are learning.

The Ixil, a Mayan culture in the Guatemalan Highlands, provides the next example of mathematics from around the world in the chapter **Math of the Maya.** Farmers in the highland village of Santa Avelina depend on their ability to grow enough corn to sustain themselves and their families. They traditionally have used application-based mathematical calculations to determine planting needs and harvesting results. In the program described in this chapter, the local students of this village are learning how to use contemporary mathematical knowledge to examine planting alternatives, thus leading to lower operating costs and greater productivity for their community. Following in their footsteps, teachers and students using this chapter can solve similar problems using measurement concepts, algebra, and probability, all situated in a rich cultural context.

Exploring mathematics with students in a Brazilian community sets the context for chapter 3, **The Streets of Ouro Preto.** Brazil's forward-looking National Educational System emphasizes interdisciplinary studies incorporating ethnomathematics. Students learn integrated concepts such as calculus, physics, and biology, and they are formally assessed on their abilities to apply them in real-life situations and communicate their findings. As described here, a group of Brazilian students are investigating mathematics along the street through the architecture, history, music, and day-to-day activities of the 300-year-old city of Ouro Preto. Guided by this chapter, their fellow students in other countries can use these investigations as a starting point for learning to better see the mathematics of their own communities and the ways in which mathematics literally helps shape their world.

Chapter 4, **Navajo Beading and Weaving Patterns,** focuses on the mathematics that arises when members of the native cultures of the American Southwest create beadwork and rug weavings. Measurement, geometry, symmetry, and the use of patterns are just a few of the mathematical connections made. The activities in this chapter enable students to learn mathematical concepts involving Euclidian geometry specific to the Cartesian grid as they apply contemporary instruction to design beadwork and rug weavings with the aid of computer software programs.

The African country of Ghana and the rich cultural artwork of the Asante people provide the context for the activities of chapter 5, **Adinkra Symbols.** These symbols are stamped across cloth by skilled artisans, and they convey traditional ideals and beliefs that connect to local proverbs. Students will explore concepts in geometry, measurement, and data analysis as they examine the many ways mathematics is used by the Asante to create art and communicate and maintain their culture.

Chapter 6, **The Game of Klappenspiel,** looks at a mathematical activity often played in German schools. Students will be challenged to develop successful problem-solving strategies as they explore simple facts, operations, and probabilities. Klappenspiel ("Shut the Box") provides a fun-filled application of probability calculations. Games of chance are popular around the world, and this is just one example of how mathematics and culture combine to influence the activities of a community.

In chapter 7, **Graffiti Shapes and Styles,** students will take a closer look at a major element of global urban culture. We have used our cultural simulations with students in many places across the United States, and graffiti has been of great interest to students wherever we go. This is not surprising, as graffiti is an artistic practice that crosses all race, class, and gender barriers. Studying it allows us to show how culture can be truly global, through examples of graffiti everywhere from Iran to Costa Rica. Focusing on legal forms of graffiti, such as the murals commissioned by the city of Philadelphia, helps to promote positive social values as well as highlight geometric traditions invented by and for the youth themselves. Making a connection between graffiti and mathematics provides a strong learning motivation for many students, particularly those in urban and inner-city settings. The mathematical connections made here include Cartesian mapping, geometry (including perimeter and area, angles, and measurement) as well as polar coordinates, linear spirals, and logarithmic spirals made using our web-based applet.

Chapter 8, **Stick Charts and Woven Fronds,** explores the mathematics of cultures from Hawaii and other islands of the South Pacific, as displayed in methods of ocean navigation that employ woven palm fronds from plants indigenous to the region. Islanders wove numerous household items, including mats, hats, and even sails for their outriggers. This ancient craft, once so prevalent, has seen a renaissance as people from these communities race to recover what was nearly a lost art. Weaving provides an active way for students to create models they can use to study measurement, patterns, and geometry. The variety of items constructed in this craft illustrates the way cultures use local materials to produce items of daily use, and this application exemplifies how culture, mathematics, and applied technology can intersect to solve everyday challenges. The revival of this once nearly dead art form itself proves the value that people place on maintaining cultural tradition and identity.

In chapter 9, **Rangolee and Kolam Folk Art Designs,** students will explore numerous mathematical concepts and properties inherent in making these creations. In India, making Rangolee and Kolam art is part of the daily activities of women from nearly all socioeconomic groups. These designs are easy to learn and easy to reproduce, and some have cultural significance and stories attached to them. The designs are based on isometric, radial, and rectangular dot matrices, and they reflect a number of mathematical concepts, including ones involving fractions, geometry, and algebra.

The art from Bulgaria depicted in chapter 10, **Embroidery Patterns,** is still practiced today, and well-made pieces draw the interest of buyers and collectors worldwide. Students will learn how geometry as art helps this unique culture maintain a cultural identity. An analysis of the Koch curve allows students in the younger grades to study sequence and patterns, and students in higher grades will be introduced to fractal geometry situated within this cultural context. Other mathematical concepts incorporated here include algebraic thinking and modeling, measurement, ratios, and proportional relationships.

In our final chapter, **Two-Sided Dice of the Potawatomi,** the game of *Kwezage'win* ("dice game") is explored. Kwezage'win is a traditional game still played by American Indian Nations in the northern United States, and it typifies the way that people around the world have used mathematics to invent and play games of chance. American Indian cultures often used "stick dice," peach pits, beaver teeth, bird bones, or two-sided disks crafted from locally gathered materials to construct objects for their games. In this chapter, students will explore probability and data analysis concepts as they connect a traditional Native American game with contemporary mathematics concepts.

As we begin our journey in the chapters that follow, we hope the reader now has a better understanding of how mathematics and culture can be intertwined in the classroom and the benefits that can result. We challenge teachers to look for our central themes— *authentic application, life in numbers,* and *intentional intelligence and use*—as they and their students participate in the activities. We believe that through such a study teachers will gain a much deeper understanding and appreciation for educating from an ethnomathematical perspective.

1

AFRICAN DIASPORA
Cornrow Hair Braiding

Locations   Communities in Africa and the African diaspora
(including the United States, Caribbean,
United Kingdom, and Brazil)

66 *Teaching with the cornrows software is deeply satisfying to me
because finally I can integrate my rich Afro-Caribbean heritage into
the mainstream pedagogy that I confer to students instead of always
separating them and feeling like my culture is not relevant.* 99

—*Audrey Grace Bennett*

Context

We might think of cornrow braids as a style made famous by today's youth, but they
began as an ancient practice from Africa. Clay sculptures with cornrows have been found
in Nigeria that date back to 500 BCE. In the original African societies, different cornrow braiding styles could express whether the person who wore it was married or single,
which religious group she was in, which family tree she was related to, the age group she
belonged to, and more (see fig. 1.1). Braiding expressed social bonds, but it also offered a
creative exploration of geometric patterns. The most basic pattern in cornrow braiding is
the way that each individual twist *(plait)* changes in size as you move along the braid. In
mathematical terms, we would say that in each step *(iteration)*, a copy of the original plait
undergoes a scaling transformation *(dilation)*.

Fig. 1.1. A girl from the Mende people of Sierra Leone. Her hairstyle indicates her rank in the Sande society, a secret organization for women (Boone 1986).

Figure 1.2 shows a geometric model for that iterative process. It might seem as though this is just imposing Western mathematics on something purely intuitive. But Africans also have a tradition of geometric modeling. Figure 1.3 shows a similar geometric simulation of cornrows in a traditional African sculpture.

Patterns that repeat themselves at different scales are called *fractals*. Fractals are a common theme in many African designs. Houses are built in circles of circles, decorative patterns use triangles with triangles, and so on. Cornrows are just one example of the fractal tradition in African design.

To make a straight braid, all you need are iterations of scaling transformations. Scaling is one of the four geometric transformations; the other three are also

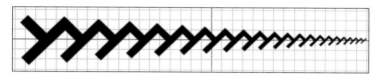

Fig. 1.2. Geometric simulation of a cornrow braid

Fig. 1.3. The expanding zigzag designs on this African sculpture show an abstraction of the scaling pattern in cornrows (Boone 1986).

used in cornrows. *Rotation* gives us curved braids, *translation* controls how closely packed the plaits will be, and *reflection* is used to make one side the mirror image of the other. When employed together with iteration, these four geometric transformations can create an astounding array of patterns, as shown in figure 1.4.

During the slave trade, Africans were stripped of their personal possessions. Certain African traditions, such as folk tales, music, and hairstyles, could be transmitted without physical goods, and retaining such traditions was a way of resisting the psychological domination of slave masters. By the 1950s, African Americans were gaining a new voice in the civil rights movement, and many black writers and artists began to look back to these "hidden" elements of cultural retention as a way to express a new pride in African heritage. One of the first to make a trip to

Fig. 1.4. A contemporary cornrow hairstyle

Africa was the artist John Biggers. He realized that the cornrow styles he had seen growing up in North Carolina were actually survivals of African tradition. In the book of drawings he published from this trip, he writes: "Many West African hair styles are worn by Negro women in the United States, including this one—'cornrows.' The hair is greased, combed, and tightly plaited. The ends of the hair that fall upon the neck are tied by a string. The comb has been carved from hard wood" (Biggers 1962, p. 99).

After the civil rights movement of the 1950s and 1960s, the growing recognition of the "African diaspora"—the common roots of black people in the U.S., Caribbean, U.K., Brazil, etc.—was accompanied by a new youth movement in the 1970s and 1980s that came to be called "hip hop." Cornrows became part of an explosion of new musical and artistic forms in many parts of what historian Paul Gilroy (1993) calls "The Black Atlantic."

Kindergarten–Grade 3

Objectives

Students will explore the numeric properties of various cornrow hairstyles. For example, the visible lengths of this style become progressively shorter from front to back: If the longest is 4 inches, the progression is 4, 3, 2, 1. More complex patterns can be found by counting the number of plaits (twists) making up each single braid, and comparing the totals for a series of braids. Finally, these numbers can be converted into different prices, as stylists will charge a higher fee for more complex styles.

Materials

- Rulers
- 3 × 5-inch index cards
- Paper strips of any color, cut in various lengths from $1/2$ inch to 3 inches (in $1/2$-inch increments)
- Glue sticks
- Web page "Transformational geometry and iteration in cornrow hairstyles" at http://csdt.rpi.edu/african/CORNROW_CURVES/index.htm

---

Standards Met in This Section

Common Core State Standards—Measurement and Data

Generate measurement data by measuring lengths of several objects to the nearest whole unit, or by making repeated measurements of the same object. Show the measurements by making a line plot, where the horizontal scale is marked off in whole-number units (2.MD.9, National Governors Association Center for Best Practices and Council of Chief State School Officers [NGA Center and CCSSO] 2010, p. 20).

NCTM Standards—Measurement

- ▲ recognize the attributes of length, volume, weight, area, and time;

- ▲ compare and order objects according to these attributes;

- ▲ understand how to measure using nonstandard and standard units; and

- ▲ select an appropriate unit and tool for the attribute being measured (NCTM 2000, p. 102).

Introduce

Many people around the world today, particular younger people and those with African heritage, wear cornrow hairstyles. These hairstyles are created by talented hair braiders who create rows of twisted or braided hair. The beauty of the style results from the particular patterns created with the braids flowing *(seriating)* around the head's contour. The lengths of the braids typically change from longer to shorter, and this constant change is where the use of mathematics becomes most noticeable and the beauty of the braiding most dramatic. The pattern of each part of a braid is repeated over and over *(iteration)* as its length slowly changes *(scaling)*.

1. Show students several photos of men and women, boys and girls wearing African cornrow hairstyles. You can find them online by using an image search for "cornrows" at a site such as Google. In many photos the subject is posing in a natural way, but to focus on geometric patterns in hair, you will want photos in which persons are photographed straight on in a style more like a "mug shot." You can find a good selection of these poses at http://csdt.rpi.edu/african/CORNROW_CURVES/index.htm by selecting "Math Software" in the menu and then clicking on the image of a woman with cornrows in the upper right corner. Explain to your students that hairstyles can be about creativity—an individual's sense of style or a new fashion—but that they can also be about the community people belong to, and the heritage in their family. Describe cornrow hair braiding as a style that is both creative and fashionable, while also coming from an African cultural tradition.

2. Show your students a how-to video for braiding. You can find these on such sites as YouTube, or select "How to Braid" in the menu of the web page mentioned in step 1. This is a good opportunity to introduce the term *plait* (a single twist or knot) and the idea that you can count how many plaits are in one braid.

3. Select one of the photos of a cornrow hairstyle (for example, fig. 1.5) and ask the students what they notice about the braids. Encourage them to discuss the repeated patterns of similarly shaped braids and how they seem to grow from longer to shorter.

4. Discuss how hair braiders earn their living braiding these styles. Prices are related to the number of plaits (knots) in each braid, the number of braids, and the complexity of the braiding pattern. Some styles can take nearly twenty-four hours to complete and can cost between $200 and $300. Show the students several styles and discuss the price that

Fig. 1.5. A drawing of cornrows by So Yoon Lym

students would suggest be charged for each example. What rationale can the students provide for determining a way to set a price for a particular style? Is it time related (longer hours cost more), length related (longer braids cost more), or some other calculation? Why might you want to braid someone's hair for free?

Explore and Create

Provide your students with paper strips that have been cut in various lengths from $1/2$ inch to 3 inches (in $1/2$-inch increments), or have them create the strips themselves. Each strip represents one plait in the braid they will create. Ask them to arrange the strips, moving from longer to shorter strips in straight or curved patterns. Note that curved patterns will require that the students overlap their pieces; remind them to create the overlap by rotating about the center. Tell them to not glue the strips to the index cards yet because they may wish to change their patterns.

Ask the students or groups of students to describe their patterns and what they were thinking as they created them. Most students will not immediately seriate the strips in increments of $1/2$ inch. Some will note they started with only the longest lengths but then discovered that their patterns became more interesting and attractive when they used all of the length increments. Work to elicit this awareness and response. Next, direct the students to glue the paper strips to the index cards so they have a physical example of their pattern that they can move and save. Ask students to share verbally or in writing what they see their pattern doing. Encourage them to use the rich mathematics vocabulary they already know.

As a final step, have students determine a price to be paid for each style. Ask the students to explain how their price was calculated either using words or with a mathematical sentence.

Apply and Extend

- Challenge students to create new patterns using different shapes that are similar yet scaled differently.

- Encourage students to explore what happens visually to the pattern when they use straight-lined patterns versus curved-lined patterns. Which do most prefer?

- Older students or those who like an extra challenge may wish to measure the lengths of their pattern rows with a scale and create a line graph to represent the various lengths.

Summarize and Assess

Discussion Questions

Q In what ways are cornrow braiders using math? Is it only in geometric form, or might numbers be used as well? Are they using math more like mathematicians, more like artists, or more like architects?

Q What other things might we see around us, either created by people or created by nature, that have repeated patterns of differing shapes and sizes?

Grades 4–8

Objectives

Students will explore geometric transformations, geometric sequences, patterns, and related algorithms through the use of an online applet as they create their own cornrow designs. The students will compare and contrast their own designs with others in the class as they seek to interpret the designs into algebraic statements through coordinate geometry. Students will look for patterns within the designs and make conjectures about the types of transformations and their related algorithms used in those designs.

Materials

- Web page "Transformational geometry and iteration in cornrow hairstyles" at http://csdt.rpi.edu/african/CORNROW_CURVES/index.htm

- Graph paper

- Notebook paper and pencil

- Calculator

- Protractor

Standards Met in This Section

Common Core State Standards—Geometry

Describe the effect of dilations, translations, rotations, and reflections on two-dimensional figures using coordinates (8.G.3, NGA Center and CCSSO 2010, p. 56).

NCTM Standards—Measurement

- ▲ use coordinate geometry to represent and examine the properties of geometric shapes;

- ▲ describe sizes, positions, and orientations of shapes under informal transformations such as flips, turns, slides, and scaling; and

- ▲ recognize and apply geometric ideas and relationships in areas outside the mathematics classroom, such as art, science, and everyday life (NCTM 2000, p. 232).

Introduce

Cornrow hairstyles are rooted in indigenous African tradition, and they also represent a vibrant part of contemporary youth culture. They are varied in form but share elements of transformational geometry, as the same pattern is repeated in the plane. Through the following exercise, students will gain information about the everyday use of such geometric transformations as rotations, translations, and reflections. The wide variety of patterns that can be designed for cornrows shows students how cultural creativity can be expressed through geometry.

Explore and Create

In pairs, have students access the web address in the Materials list, and ask them to click on "Tutorial" in the applet's menu to learn how to use iterative geometric transformations to simulate cornrows. Note that the scaling and rotation tutorial pages include some follow-up questions to make sure the students understand how numbers control the transformation (such as scaling as percentage, and rotation as angle change).

Next, have the students select "Math Software" in the applet menu. This will allow them to make their own cornrow designs. Tell the students to print out their designs, or to use graph paper to sketch their designs for later discussion.

Have students record the patterns they observe in their designs. This recording should first be done through the use of language as they describe the patterns. Students can then use the language of mathematics to describe those patterns. This language can refer to geometric transformations (translation, rotation, dilation, reflection), the measures those transformations act upon (position, angle, length), or even algebraic expressions to describe relations between a series of braids. For example, figure 1.6 shows a design where each side has thirteen braids at evenly spaced angles through a sweep of 90 degrees. Students who carry out this simulation should be able to confirm that they are placed every 7.5 degrees, because 90/12 = 7.5.

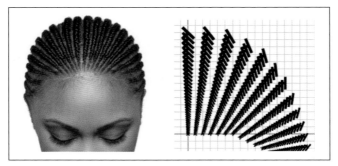

Fig. 1.6. Original cornrow design with its graphic simulation

Apply and Extend

- Have students compare their designs with those created by other students. They should be encouraged to look for similarities across their designs and the ways those similarities are described algebraically.

- Student can also propose questions or challenges. For example, figure 1.7 shows a circle of 36 plaits. What rotation is required in each iteration to create a circle? What rotation is required for n plaits?

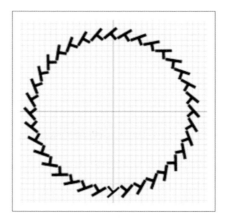

Fig. 1.7. Thirty-six plaits at 10° rotations = 360 degrees

- Have students record the values used to simulate successive braids across the same hairstyle. What changes are made as you move from braid to braid?

Summarize and Assess

Discussion Questions

Q   Why did some parameters change from braid to braid, while others remained constant?

Q   Can you create a design that would be difficult or impossible to make in real hair?

Q   Reflection symmetry usually occurs in making braids on one side of the head identical to the other. In these simulations it would be across the y-axis. Can you make designs using reflection across the x-axis? Both axes?

Grades 9–12

Objectives

Students will use an online applet to create the program for a cornrow design. They will write a script in which each step in the algorithm is explicitly formulated. Students will create geometric sequences using the applet and illustrate their patterns with algorithmic and visual pattern sequence.

Materials

- Web page "Transformational geometry and iteration in cornrow hairstyles" at http://csdt.rpi.edu/african/CORNROW_CURVES/index.htm
- Graph paper
- Notebook paper and pencil
- Calculator
- Protractor

Standards Met in This Section

Common Core State Standards—Geometry

Apply geometric methods to solve design problems (e.g., designing an object or structure to satisfy physical constraints or minimize cost; working with typographic grid systems based on ratios) (G-MG.3, NGA Center and CCSSO 2010, p. 78).

NCTM Standards—Measurement

- ▲ analyze properties and determine attributes of two- and three-dimensional objects;
- ▲ explore relationships (including congruence and similarity) among classes of two- and three-dimensional geometric objects, make and test conjectures about them, and solve problems involving them;

Introduce

One challenge faced when including indigenous cultural materials in the classroom is that they often seem like obscure museum artifacts. Cornrow hairstyles have the advantage of being rooted in tradition while still being part of contemporary youth subculture. Thus they are a great way to bring the relevance of indigenous knowledge into the classroom. In addition, they are so varied in form, and yet composed of discrete elements (the individual plaits making up each braid), which offers an opportunity for showing how cultural creativity can be expressed through geometric innovation (see fig. 1.8). Fractal scaling sequences are evident in a wide variety of African designs and artistic efforts. Examining cornrow hair braiding as an example of mathematics applied in cultural activities also provides students with a glimpse into the African tradition of using fractal structure.

Fig. 1.8. A more complicated cornrow hairstyle

Explore and Create

The menu for the web page on the Materials list contains a "Culture" section, a "Tutorial" section, and two applets: the "Math Software" applet, which uses numeric parameters only, and the "Programming Software" applet, which allows students to create their own algorithms.

We recommend starting with the "Culture" section of the website, which contains four topics within the history of cornrow braiding: "African Origins," "Middle Passage," "Civil War to Civil Rights," and "Hip Hop." Divide the students into four groups, and have each group look over one of the four sections of cultural background. Then have them report on what they found out about the history of cornrow braiding.

Ask the students to move on to the "Tutorial" section of the web page. The tutorial will ask them to solve a challenge on each page. Have the class decide as a whole what value is best for each page.

Now move to the "Math Software" applet. Students can simulate the braiding samples on the page or else design their own. They can experiment with the use of mathematics to describe their observed patterns. For example, in the braid in figure 1.9, the plaits are scaled down by 90 percent in each iteration. The first, which we can call plait 0, has a height of 80 units. So the next, which we can call plait 1, is 90 percent of 80, which is 72. Note that plait 7 is just a little less than half the height of plait 0; it is 38 units high, because $80 \times 0.9^7 = 38$. This could then be generalized: The nth plait has a height of 80×0.9^n. Using similar relations of width rather than height, the length of the entire braid can be calculated as the sum of a geometric sequence.

Fig. 1.9. Scaling by 90 percent in each iteration

Students can examine the patterns produced as continuous curves. You can first introduce the question using figure 1.10, which asks students to think about which arc would be a better fit to the curves in this cornrow hairstyle. The answer is the arc of a logarithmic spiral.

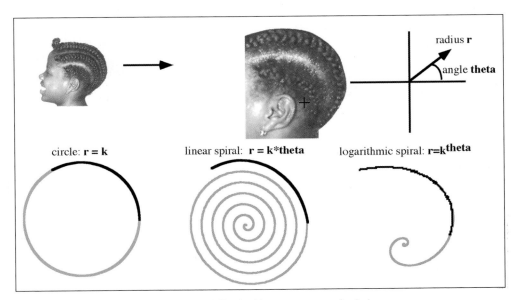

Fig. 1.10. Modeling braid curves as arcs of spirals

The next step is to actually measure the radius at selected angles of theta. In the example of figure 1.11, we have provided the protractor, so students will only need a ruler. But any cornrows photo or cornrows simulation can be used along with a protractor.

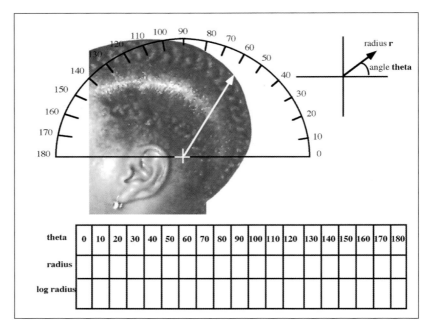

theta	0	10	20	30	40	50	60	70	80	90	100	110	120	130	140	150	160	170	180
radius																			
log radius																			

Fig. 1.11. Measuring change of angle with change of radius in braid curves

Plotting the increase of radius with increasing theta will produce a curved graph. To change this into a linear graph we need to use the logarithmic function:

$y = a^x$ expressed as $\log y = x \bullet \log a$. The logarithmic spiral $r = k^{\text{theta}}$ becomes $\log r =$ theta $\bullet \log k$. Putting this into the form for a linear graph, $y = m \bullet x + b$, we have $y = \log r$; $x =$ theta; $m = \log k$; and $b = 0$. So all we have to do is measure the slope m of a plot of theta versus $\log r$. Since $m = \log k$, then $k = 10m$.

If you plot a logarithmic spiral using this value for k, it should closely match the curvature of the cornrow braid. You can test your solution visually by plugging these values into a graphing calculator or into an online applet such as the one at http://www.univie.ac.at/future.media/moe/galerie/geom3/geom3.html.

Apply and Extend

- Now try out the "Programming Software" applet. Have students experiment with adding color to braids (see the examples in figs. 1.12 and 1.13).

- In the programmable applet, the braid is generated through an *iterative loop*. Ask students to use a loop inside of a loop to generate entire sequences of braids and other patterns. If you find the scaling exponent for the logarithmic curve in a sequence of braids, does that remain the same, or does it change?

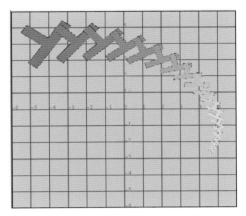

Fig. 1.12. Programmable cornrows applet adding iteration across the color spectrum

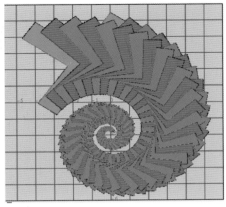

Fig. 1.13. Programmable cornrows applet alternating in color for each iteration

- Using the other applets at http://csdt.rpi.edu, explore some other occurrences of scaling patterns in African design: fractals in architecture (http://csdt.rpi.edu/african/African_Fractals/); and iterative transforms in Mangbetu sculpture (http://csdt.rpi.edu/african/MANG_DESIGN/culture/mang_homepage.html), and so on.

Summarize and Assess

Discussion Questions

Q Why have cornrow braids become more complex in more recent versions?

Q How can we use mathematics to define what we mean by "complex"?

Q What other examples of logarithmic spirals, fractals, and additional scaling patterns exist in natural or cultural structures?

Featured Consultant for This Chapter

Audrey Grace Bennett, *an associate professor of graphics at Rensselaer Polytechnic Institute, provided the inspiration and much of the content for exploring the relationship between mathematics and cornrow hair braiding. She has an MFA in graphic design from Yale's School of Art and a BA in studio art from Dartmouth.*

2

GUATEMALA
Math of the Maya

Location   A small mountain village in western Guatemala

66*Our people, the Maya, have been growing corn for as long as we have been a people. To our people, corn is everything. I am happy to see that students in our school are learning mathematics in situations that they experience at home and in the community. This helps them understand that math is part of everything.*99

—*Lucas Sánchez (at left in photo)*

Context

Santa Avelina is a small rural Mayan community nestled in the highlands of Guatemala. Most villagers speak Ixil, which is one of the more than twenty current Mayan languages, and some of them speak Spanish. The community is composed of about three thousand people whose lives center on the growing of corn. In Santa Avelina there is no industry, and ecotourism is just beginning to take hold. Farming in Santa Avelina is very different from what many others experience throughout the country. The majority of productive land is owned by a small minority of the population while only a small minority of the indigenous workers own the land they till. Many farms consist of large commercialized plantations where only one type of crop is grown, typically for export. This form of farming often exploits the land and environment because the flow of natural elements through the ecosystem is interrupted. Access to a secure and affordable food supply is frequently a challenge for workers and their families, as they often have to travel from plantation to plantation to follow the harvests.

Families in Santa Avelina subsist on the corn they grow and the few chickens or pigs they raise. Corn is everything in the village. Villagers employ a type of permaculture where a focus on ecological sustainability relies on traditional and contemporary agricultural practices. Farmers plant several crops such as beans and corn together, so that one crop (the beans, in this example) can naturally replenish nutrients in the soil depleted by the corn. Productivity is increased with fewer invasive and non-ecological practices.

People grind the corn they grow to make tortillas, which they eat at every meal and also boil in warm water to make a drink enjoyed by young and old alike. Excess corn may be used to feed the animals. What is then left can be sold in the market to produce additional income for the family to purchase other required items.

Education is valued in the village, yet not all children are able to attend school. Some families cannot afford to get by without the labor that even young children can provide. Village children fortunate enough to be allowed to go to school have several educational choices. Students may attend a local public school where the language of instruction is Spanish and the curriculum does not include overt Mayan cultural connections. Another possibility is the William Botnan School, an alternative school where parents and sponsors contribute money to provide the funds required to run it. In the Botnan School, students in pre-K–grade 6 experience bilingual immersion education. In the youngest grades, students learn first in their home language of Ixil, with an emphasis on connecting the curriculum with actual village life. In each ensuing year, more Spanish immersion is included. At the end of grade 6, most students have completed all the schooling they will receive, and they have the advantage of fluently reading, writing, and speaking in two languages. They also have gained knowledge in school that has real application in their lives within the community.

Lucas Sánchez is a local agricultural agent of Mayan descent who works with area farmers to help answer their questions and increase their harvests. He also serves as a bridge between agriculture in the village and the teachers and students at the immersion school. Lucas shares his expertise in the school as he describes career opportunities for students and the types of knowledge and skills a scientist such as himself needs. Teachers in the village often use this background information to create a context for the subject information they teach. As Lucas describes the multiple ways in which mathematics is used in planting, growing, and harvesting corn, students learn skills and knowledge they can apply in real-life settings. After participating in a mathematics and corn-growing activity, one student exclaimed, "I cannot wait until I go home and can tell my father how he can grow more corn!"

Kindergarten–Grade 3

Objectives

Students draw maps of garden plots to explore concepts of measurement, addition, and subtraction. They will use their maps as they calculate seed need and cost, as related to the amount of corn produced using traditional and nontraditional spacing standards for planting.

Materials

- Measuring tape or meter stick
- Paper and pencil
- Yarn or string

Standards Met in This Section

Common Core State Standards—Number and Operations in Base Ten

Fluently add and subtract with values using strategies based on place value, properties of operations, and/or the relationship between addition and subtraction (3.NBT.2, National Governors Association Center for Best Practices and Council of Chief State School Officers [NGA Center and CCSSO] 2010, p. 24).

NCTM Standards—Number and Operations

- ▲ develop a sense of whole numbers and represent and use them in flexible ways, including relating, composing, and decomposing numbers;

- ▲ understand situations that entail multiplication and division, such as equal groupings of objects and sharing equally; and

- ▲ develop and use strategies for whole-number computations, with a focus on addition and subtraction (NCTM 2000, p. 78).

NCTM Standards—Measurement

- ▲ understand how to measure using nonstandard and standard units (NCTM 2000, p. 102).

Introduce

Farmers in the highlands of Guatemala typically have their own *milpas* (corn fields) where the grow corn and other crops. These fields are most often set in a square shape that farmers call a *cuerda,* which measures approximately 20 meters long and 20 meters wide. (In some other Spanish-speaking countries, the word *cuerda* refers to an area slightly under one acre.) The measurements are usually not exact, as the farmers consider a man's step to roughly equal one meter. Using steps and a piece of rope or string, farmers step out and mark the edges of their milpas and the twenty rows in each across their fields. Traditionally, farmers have planted mounds of corn one step (roughly one meter) apart. This measurement standard was handed down from father to son. In each mound they planted at least three seeds to increase the chances that one seed would germinate and grow. Corn seeds are a favorite food for birds and rodents, and the corn can be spoiled by fungus. Nearly one-third of the corn that is produced never makes it to the farmer's table.

Lucas Sánchez, the village agricultural agent, is teaching farmers that they can grow more corn if they plant their mounds closer together in each row. He recommends that they still plant each row one meter apart, but that they plant the mounds within the row 40 centimeters apart from each other. This distance still allows farmers to hoe between the mounds as the corn sprouts and grows, yet not all farmers are willing to try this newly suggested technique. Some prefer to continue growing as they always have because that is the way they know best—a common response whenever new ideas are suggested. Lucas patiently explains to those farmers willing to listen the new ideas being generated through contemporary science. As the local students of the village explore and discuss the issue and learn skills within a real-life context, they can see how what they are learning could be used to improve the living conditions of their families and community.

Explore and Create

In your own classroom, you can lead students to consider the best way to plant their own imagined milpas through the following steps:

1. Discuss with your students the problem's context and the role that growing and harvesting corn plays in this community. Discuss the types of standard units of measurement used in this village (including metric units such as a meter) and the nonstandard approximation of one person's step. Draw the length of one meter on the floor or mark a length with tape. Ask each student to "step" the line and count how many steps each student requires. Raise concepts such as "half-steps." The nonstandard ways that students explain distances other than one whole step demonstrate how an individual may measure things differently than a community measures—for instance, an individual's measurement is typically proportionate to a body part. Chart this student data.

2. Ask students to first estimate and then count the number of heel-to-toe steps it takes for each to walk the meter line. Chart both numbers. Compare data from both the steps and the heel-to-toe measurements. Ask students why their measurements vary. What could they do as a class to ensure that when measuring they all get the same values? Introduce the terms *standard* and *nonstandard* measurement as you describe the need within a community for a common standard. Explain how metric measurement is a standard used in many places throughout the world. Illustrate how a meter is further divided into smaller divisions of 10 and 100, and name these units (decimeters and centimeters).

3. Use yarn or string in a large open area to have students mark out a milpa (planting plot) in the traditional size of one cuerda. A cuerda typically is 20 meters long and 20 meters wide. Ask the students a variety of questions about its construction: What tools should they select to make their measurements? Should they use their steps or select a common tool? How can they be sure that their milpa resembles a square?

4. Students who have created the milpa model will be better prepared to visualize a milpa and draw a representative map. Discuss with them how they would measure where to place each row if the rows need to be parallel and spaced one meter apart. How many rows will their milpa contain? Students can act this out as a problem-solving strategy.

If they count the top and bottom rows, they should have a total of 21 rows. On the board, construct a map of a milpa as you ask students to draw their own map. Keep reminding them of the milpa's dimensions. Measurements between rows do not need to be exact as long as they have the same number of rows.

5. Discuss the farmer's problem of deciding whether to plant mounds one meter apart as is done traditionally, or 40 centimeters apart as Lucas suggests. How can the class determine the best choice? Assume that if three seeds are planted in a mound, one stalk of corn will grow and produce two ears of corn. Corn seed must be purchased, but it is not overly expensive. Assume each seed costs 1 cent and each ear of corn sells for 5 cents. The questions to answer include:

(a) How much seed is needed to plant the milpa with mounds one meter apart?

(b) How much seed is needed to plant the milpa with mounds 40 centimeters apart?

(c) How much corn will be produced in the milpa with traditionally spaced mounds?

(d) How much corn will be produced in the milpa with mounds 40 centimeters apart?

Have students work in pairs to apply their own strategies for determining either only (a) and (b) or else all of these questions, depending on the students' level. Students should complete their problems on the page where they drew their milpa map. After calculating an answer and displaying their work, they should write a short explanation of how they solved their answer and which measurement they would use if they wanted to grow a lot of corn. Have students chart the data and discuss the results. As a class, have students decide which measurement would be best to use.

Apply and Extend

- Challenge students to calculate the cost of seed when planting the milpa with a spacing of one meter and with a spacing of 40 centimeters.

- Challenge students to calculate the amount of corn they can expect to harvest if every mound produces two ears of corn when mounds are 40 centimeters versus one meter apart.

- Does the increased harvest when using the 40-centimeter plant spacing justify the increased cost of corn seed?

Summarize and Assess

Discussion Questions

Q If a community has used a particular solution for a long time, should they ever change to a new solution?

Q Why do you think some village farmers hesitated to adapt to new ideas?

Q Do you think it is helpful for students to learn mathematics through applications involving real-world situations?

Grades 4–8

Objectives

Students will use the number operations of multiplication and division as they explore the use of traditional spacing standards and the newly suggested spacing standards for the corn crops. They will extend their understanding of variables and algebraic notation as they express the calculations of seed spacing and related production.

Materials

- Graph paper
- Notebook paper and pencil
- Calculator
- Ruler or straightedge

Standards Met in This Section

Common Core State Standards—Operations and Algebraic Thinking

Multiply or divide to solve word problems involving multiplicative comparison, e.g., by using drawings and equations with a symbol for the unknown number to represent the problem, distinguishing multiplicative comparison from additive comparison.

Solve multistep word problems posed with whole numbers and having whole-number answers using the four operations, including problems in which remainders must be interpreted. Represent these problems using equations with a letter standing for the unknown quantity. Assess the reasonableness of answers using mental computation and estimation strategies including rounding (4.OA.2 and 3, NGA Center and CCSSO 2010, p. 29).

NCTM Standards—Number and Operations

- ▲ understand various meanings of multiplication and division; and
- ▲ use the associative and commutative properties of addition and multiplication and the distributive property of multiplication over addition to simplify computations with integers, fractions, and decimals (NCTM 2000, pp. 148 and 214).

NCTM Standards—Algebra

- ▲ use symbolic logic to represent situations and to solve problems;
- ▲ judge the meaning, utility, and reasonableness of the results of symbol manipulations, including those carried out by technology; and
- ▲ model and solve contextualized problems using various representations, such as graphs, tables, and equations (NCTM 2000, p. 222).

Introduce

Corn, or maize, has become (along with rice and wheat) one of the three staple grains that feeds the world. Maize is one of man's greatest accomplishments and is today the most versatile of all the grains. It was first domesticated in the warm, fertile valleys of Central America and Mexico. Maize is referenced in the Popul Vuh, the sacred book of the Quiche Indians of Guatemala, as early as the eighth century. Maize can be yellow, white, red, or black, and each of the colors is associated with a part of the Mayan cosmovision: *yellow* references the life-giving water; *white,* the wind; *red,* the sun, essential to the growth of the corn; and *black,* soil from Mother Earth (see fig. 2.1).

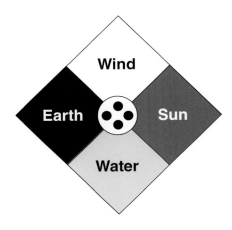

Fig. 2.1. Representation of the Mayan cosmovision

Maize is still grown as a staple for families in the highlands of Guatemala. Methods that combine ancient wisdom with modern technologies can provide farmers with a better harvest from their fields. Maize is grown in all types of terrain, and milpas (corn fields) are often located on steep hillsides. Growing enough maize to feed their families is crucial for the Maya farmers. They use the produce to feed their families and their animals and for trading to provide other essentials. The approximate yield, per 3 meters of a row, is 5 to 10 pounds of corn, or 10 to 20 ears. The amount needed per person is approximately 20 to 30 pounds or 40 to 60 ears per season. Traditionally, seeds are typically planted in hills of 3 to 4 seeds planted one meter apart with rows also separated by approximately a meter. Recently, agricultural consultants began to recommend the farmers plant the mounds more closely together (40 centimeters apart). Farmers who have for generations held to the one-meter distance between mounds are skeptical about trying the closer planting suggestion.

Explore and Create

Have students work in pairs, using graph paper to map the location of the seeds in a typical row and placing the coordinates (0, 0) as a beginning point for the planting at the (left) start of a row. Students should make a representation for the seed planting using a 40-centimeter distance for planting each mound. Beginning at the origin (0, 0) and moving to the right .40 of a unit (the meter), coordinates will occur as an arithmetic sequence: (.40, 0), (.80, 0), (1.20, 0), (1.60, 0), etc. Have students record the coordinates for each of the seed mounds and make a conjecture about the coordinates if the planting is continued from (0,0) to the right.

Using the graph of row one, extend the graph to include a second row at a one-meter distance above the first row. Beginning at the origin (0, 0), the coordinates will follow a pattern of (.40, 1), (.80, 1), (1.20, 1), (1.60, 1), etc.

Students can then examine the graphing and extend the mapping using the same pattern to include additional seed mound plantings to complete the row. A row is typically 20 meters long.

Students in the lower grades of this grade band should write the coordinates in a table and use the information to write their observations in words. The planting sequence can be continued with additional coordinates that use the sequential pattern they have established.

Students in the upper grades of the grade band can use their tables to write algebraic statements to indicate the pattern of movement, such as $X(n) = .4(n - 1)$ where n = number of the term in the sequence, and $Y(p) = (p - 1)$ where p = the number of the row.

Apply and Extend

- Have students examine the algebraic statements for the seed locations and determine if the sequence is arithmetic, geometric, or neither, and provide a rationale for their solution.

- Using the number of seed hills as determined, students should find the number of corn plants per row (three plants per mound) and express the number algebraically.

- Have students algebraically express the number of expected ears of corn per row (two ears of corn are typically harvested per mound) using calculations from above.

Summarize and Assess

Discussion Questions

Q What may be a reason why village farmers traditionally plant in cuerdas measuring 20 meters by 20 meters?

Q How might mathematical calculations be used by agricultural agents to help traditional farmers understand the use of newly recommended growing practices?

Q How would you change the design of the corn field, or milpa, planting from one year to the next to avoid wearing out the soil?

Grades 9–12

Objectives

Students will create mathematical models to explore the relationship corn planting and production has with crop loss due to disease, rot, and insects, and they will use this information to determine final yields. Students will then suggest ways to reduce waste and increase productivity and model possible related outcomes.

Materials

- Graph paper
- Notebook paper and pencil
- Calculator

Standards Met in This Section
Common Core State Standards—Statistics and Probability
Weigh the possible outcomes of a decision by assigning probabilities to payoff values and finding expected values (S-MD.5, NGA Center and CCSSO 2010, p. 83).
NCTM Standards—Algebra
▲ draw reasonable conclusions about a situation being modeled (NCTM 2000, p. 296).
NCTM Standards—Data Analysis and Probability
▲ compute and interpret the expected values of random variables in simple cases (NCTM 2000, p. 324).

Introduce

Lucas Sánchez, the agricultural agent for the village of Santa Avelina in the highlands of Guatemala, works to teach skills to local farmers who are constantly toiling to improve their production and reduce spoilage and waste. These particular farmers are fortunate in that they do not work for any collective; they typically own their own land and therefore can make their own decisions about how they plant and what they will charge. It is anything but an easy life, and farmers can usually be seen walking to their fields at daybreak, after which they will spend many hours weeding and tilling the soil.

The tending of their farm plot is nearly all done by hand. These cuerdas (20 × 20-meter squares) often are stand-alone patches cut out of the forest. Farmers create rows in which they plant seeds in mounds. Mounds for planting seeds are located anywhere from one meter to 40 centimeters apart, and the rows are located one meter apart. With a wry smile, Lucas says, "We always plant at least three seeds in a mound. One is for the birds, one is for the rats, and the last is for the people!" While farmers can see some humor in that comment, it also illustrates the many difficulties they face.

Farming successfully is a critical challenge local farmers face every growing season. Most farmers must rely on what they grow themselves to provide food for their family, feed their animals, and—with any luck—have a surplus to sell in order to buy other necessities. Lucas indicates that on average nearly one-third of what a farmer grows never makes it to the dinner table or market stall. The challenges of planting and growing do not stop after the corn is harvested, as the farmers must now face spoilage from fungus or infestation damage due to rats as the corn is stored.

Students in this activity will model production and spoilage in their own cuerda with mounds planted one meter apart in one and 40 centimeters apart in the other. They will then calculate the amount of product typically spoiled. Finally, they will suggest strategies for reducing spoilage and also calculate the amount of the improved harvest.

Explore and Create

Discuss with students the farming practices in this rural Guatemalan village, where nearly all that one eats comes from what can be harvested or grown. Students should gain an impression of how "close to the edge" many of these families live as a result of their required reliance on subsistence farming.

Divide the students in pairs, and have them use graph paper to draw a representation model of their cuerda measuring 20 meters wide and 20 meters long. The cuerdas typically stand alone and do not border other farmers' areas.

Students should model in a diagram the planting of corn in mounds 40 centimeters distant across each row. Tell students that they should estimate that each mound produces three ears of corn, and ask them to calculate and record in the chart below (table 2.1) the total harvest in ears of corn from the cuerdas.

Table 2.1
Corn harvest chart

Number of Mounds	Total Ears of Corn Produced	Corn Harvest after Spoilage

Apply and Extend

- Challenge students to write a simple algebraic algorithm that describes the amount of the harvest when the number of mounds (and productivity) is known along with the number of mounds in a cuerda.

- Challenge your students to edit their algebraic algorithm to now include the average percentage of spoilage ($1/3$) that decreases the amount of usable harvest. Ask students to record their final calculation in the previous chart.

- Ask students to discuss options and encourage them to read outside of class or communicate with experts they may locate to achieve realistic proposals. Discuss how feasible their proposals might be. For instance, a student could suggest that the harvested corn be placed in newly purchased metal silos that are ventilated and rodent proof. While this might be a solution in an affluent society, it is not a realistic proposition in Guatemala. The cost of such a silo is incomprehensible to a farmer whose family lives on a few quetzals (the Guatemalan currency worth about twelve U.S. cents) a day. And even if a few farmers could afford to buy such a silo, getting it shipped and hauled up the mountain would be nearly impossible. This is not intended to disparage the local farmers, who do well in spite of the challenges they face. The purpose is to get students to consider a context very different from their own and to arrive at suitable suggestions within that context.

- Students should then estimate the reduction of spoilage as a result of their proposal. If several teams are involved, each team can calculate their new harvest (using the algorithms they created) and compare them with the traditional losses and the projected harvests from the other teams. Class data can be charted and discussed.

Summarize and Assess

Discussion Questions

Q We have used mathematics in this activity to investigate a real social issue. How does using mathematics as a tool for investigation leading to social change affect the way we think about mathematics as a subject and about ourselves as students of mathematics?

Q What are some other examples of using mathematics to investigate social issues and using mathematics as a tool for problem solving?

Q How do we feel about our own mathematical capabilities when we are challenged to create our own algorithms to solve problems?

Featured Consultant for This Chapter

Lucas Sánchez *is an agricultural consultant for rural Mayan farmers in villages in the highlands of Guatemala. Lucas shares his expertise with community members to improve farming efficiency and also shares his mathematical knowledge with students in local classrooms.*

3

BRAZIL
The Streets of Ouro Preto

Location   The historic city of Ouro Preto, located in the southeastern Brazilian state Minas Gerais

“ *If mathematics is a universal language, then, just as in English, there are accents, and different terms used or emphasized from one country to another. In Brazil, students learn to create their own mathematical poems using mathematical modeling.* ”

— *Daniel Orey (left) and Milton Rosa (right)*

Context

Brazil is the largest country in South America and the fifth most populated country in the world, with a population of nearly 200,000,000. It is a country of rich natural environments and resources, diverse cultures, and one of the world's fastest growing, most robust economies. Brazil will receive special attention around the world through its hosting of the World Cup in 2014 and the Summer Olympics in 2016.

Educational systems in Brazil are evolving to reflect the country's vibrant economic and social growth. They present an effective, futuristic model for other educational systems around the world—a stark contrast to what happened from the mid-1960s to 1990 when Brazil was governed by a military political dictatorship that restricted free speech and opposing political views. Educational change is underway in Brazil, and while significant challenges remain, efforts to design a world-class educational system where all children realize their fullest potential are being implemented. One such government program applied at the national level is called *bolsa escola*. Grants are provided to economically disadvantaged parents to keep their children in schools.

Brazil's forward-looking National Educational System emphasizes interdisciplinary studies that incorporate ethnomathematics—the dynamic and evolving study of relationships between mathematics and cultures. Ubiratan D'Ambrosio, a Brazilian mathematical scholar and philosopher, has played a leading role in the research and development of mathematics education, particularly as it relates to culture. Sparked by his efforts, ethnomathematics has gained international recognition and acceptance. Brazilian mathematics students are now learning to apply integrated concepts (calculus, physics, biology, etc.) in real-life situations, find solutions, support their conclusions, and express their findings. Students are assessed on their knowledge and solutions to the everyday problems posed in their programs of study. Federal law in Brazil has recently required that school curriculums infuse connections to Brazil's African heritage in all subject areas, including mathematics, as a way to value this rich cultural background.

Children in Brazil must prepare for assessments that require all students to know a second or third language, communicate findings, and use mathematics in contextual settings including calculus, physics, biology, etc. Recently, students were asked to discuss the problem of water resources and usage in Brazil and propose solutions. Students are ranked by performance on such tests and, if they do well, are eligible to enter a federal university (comparable to the University of California system) for free. For this reason, students and teachers take their interdisciplinary studies incorporating ethnomathematics seriously.

Ouro Preto, the location explored in this chapter, is a picturesque 300-year-old city in eastern Brazil. Students in local schools are exploring mathematics by investigating the city's architecture, history, music, and day-to-day activities. These Brazilian students learn to appreciate the mathematics of their communities and the ways in which mathematics literally helps to shape their world. Through following and retracing their steps, students in other communities will better understand the crucial and often hidden mathematics that are the foundation of their own world as they seek out these mathematical connections in an everyday setting.

Kindergarten–Grade 3

Objectives

Students will integrate pattern analysis, algebra, and measurement concepts to explore and document house-numbering systems. Once they understand how maps, street, and house numbers are constructed to meet cultural expectations, students will create their own patterns to challenge their peers.

Materials

- Measuring tape or stick with metric measurements
- Paper, pencils, and crayons (or other drawing tools)
- Lengths of string

Introduce

Ouro Preto, a 300-year-old Brazilian community and a UNESCO World Cultural site, preserves the largest collection of Baroque architecture in the Western Hemisphere. This city of more than 70,000 people offers numerous opportunities to explore mathematics through its architecture, history, music, and day-to-day activities. One such opportunity is exploring how houses are numbered along its streets.

Many students believe that the numbering systems we use to mark homes or buildings today have always been the norm. This is not historically true—in fact, the earliest such systems were invented in the early 1600s to indicate individual residences built along the Pont Notre-Dame in Paris. Streets had names at that time, but without separate numbers confusion reigned. The Parisian houses were not numbered to help messengers deliver communications or parcels; instead, numbers were used to help people identify their homes from those of their neighbors, because all houses along the street were similar in size and shape!

As cities grew and populations expanded, a variety of numbering systems developed around the world, based on the cultures and preferences of those who lived there. Some systems ordered the numbers of homes with even numbers on one side of the street (e.g., *2, 4, 6*) and odd numbers on the opposite side (*1, 3, 5,* and so on). In Britain, a different system was used, and homes were numbered consecutively starting with 1 and extending up one side of the street and then around and back down the other sides.

House-numbering systems provide rich opportunities for exploring number systems and measurement concepts. Daniel Orey, a mathematics professor in Ouro Preto, was invited to observe an exercise in a local school district in the rural town of Coelhos, located about 18 miles (30 km) from Ouro Preto. Students were brought together from rural areas to walk a "math trail" constructed in their one-street town of at most fifty buildings. Most homes had no numbers at all. Elementary students had drawn maps of the *aldea* (town) to show houses marked with the names of those living there. A few homes did have numbers, but there was no apparent order to the numbering system. The students' teacher organized an investigation of house-numbering systems and asked the students to write letters to the town mayor proposing a system for a new numbering system for the community. The result was a success—the mayor agreed with the students' plan, and he sent workers out to place numbers on all the buildings in the town!

In Ouro Preto, residents created yet another system of home numbering that provides the basis for our investigation. Daniel, working with students in his community, posed the following question: "Why is the first house on Rua Alvarenga given number 7? Why not 0 or 1?" The students pondered this and discussed many possible reasons. Some of the ideas that surfaced related to measurement, and so one group of students measured the distance from the middle of the door to the start of the street with string. They then divided that length by seven (the house number), and they were amazed to discover that one-seventh of the distance was not quite a meter but was close to one. With further investigation, the students learned that in 1875 Brazil became one of the first nations to adopt the newly developed metric system. Prior to that, a cultural system several centuries old had been used. The length they had discovered was called a *barras,* and it was related to an emperor who once standardized the measurement system using his body parts.

Explore and Create

1. With your students, discuss their own house numbers and what system their community uses to name and number streets and houses. Are houses in the northern part of town numbered differently than those in the south? Ask students to draw a map of their street that includes their house as they envision it. They should include the street name or number and as many of their neighbors' house numbers as they can remember. Can they see a pattern or a system used to identify where they and others in their community live?

2. Ask each student to draw his or her house on a piece of paper without including an address or house number on the picture. Place several lengths of string or yarn along the classroom floor to depict a roadway. Place the house pictures along the length of string or yarn with houses spaced equally. Select a student whose foot size will be used as a standard measurement for this next activity. Draw a line around the student's foot on a piece of paper, and replicate it enough times so that each student has one "foot-print." Select one end of the street and number your new street based on the number of units (foot-prints) each house is from the end of the street. For instance, suppose that moving down the street from left to right takes eight "feet" to get from the starting point to the first house. Eight becomes the number for this house. On a small slip of paper, number this house and continue on measuring and numbering the successive houses in the same way.

Have students draw a map of their newly numbered street and write a short description of how these houses were numbered. Is there a pattern in their numbering system?

3. Use the following template (fig. 3.1) to explore house numbering using number patterns.

Fig. 3.1. Template for house numbering patterns

If a numbering sequence begins with *1, 3, 6* (left to right), what do students think the successive numbers will be? Ask them to share their ideas and justify their thinking.

4. Can students write a number sentence or algorithm that represents the calculation for each successive number in the pattern when *x* is the variable that represents the number of the first house? For example, in the *1, 3, 6* number pattern the algorithm for determining the next number after 1 is to add 2. If we represent the first number on the sequence as *x,* then the second number is *x* + 2, or 3. What is the algorithm for the house number *6*?

Apply and Extend

- Challenge students to create a house number pattern different from the one already presented. Can students stump their peers with an especially clever and challenging number pattern?

Summarize and Assess

Discussion Questions

Q   In this activity, we have learned how history and mathematics are often integrated. What are other examples where the culture of a community affects the way mathematics is used there?

Q   Numbers were used in variety of ways in this house-numbering activity. How would we define or explain these types of numbers—ordinal, nominal, and cardinal? What kinds of numbers do the house numbers represent?

Grades 4–8

Objectives

Students will use the number operations of multiplication and division as they explore measurements in the streets of Ouro Preto. They will practice computation skills, learn to make reasonable estimates, and compare standard and nonstandard measurements. Students will also represent and analyze the mathematical situations presented through expressions and equations that use algebraic symbols. They will use the given information in mathematical models to represent and understand relationships between the standard and nonstandard measurements.

Materials

- Notebook paper and pencil
- Graph paper
- Ruler or straightedge
- Colored pencils (three, any color)
- Calculator

Standards Met in This Section
Common Core State Standards—Expressions and Equations
Write and evaluate numerical expressions involving whole-number exponents.
Understand solving an equation or inequality as a process of answering a question: which values from a specified set, if any, make the equation or inequality true? Use substitution to determine whether a given number in a specified set makes an equation or inequality true (6.EE.1 and 5, NGA Center and CCSSO 2010, pp. 43–44).
NCTM Standards—Number and Operations
▲ understand various meanings of multiplication and division;   ▲ understand the effects of multiplying and dividing whole numbers; and   ▲ understand the meaning and effects of arithmetic operations with fractions, decimals, and integers (NCTM 2000, pp. 148, 214).
NCTM Standards—Measurement
▲ understand both metric and customary systems of measurement;   ▲ understand relationships among units and convert from one unit to another within the same system; and   ▲ use common benchmarks to select appropriate methods for estimating measurements (NCTM 2000, p. 240).
NCTM Standards—Algebra
▲ represent and analyze patterns and functions, using words, tables, and graphs;   ▲ represent the idea of an unknown quantity using a letter or a symbol;   ▲ express mathematical relationships using equations; and   ▲ use symbolic algebra to represent situations and solve problems, especially those that involve linear relationships (NCTM 2000, pp. 158, 222).

Introduce

Very young children can begin to express measurements through common everyday objects. These objects that are familiar to them provide a standard for comparison. Often the comparative object is a part of the body, such as the length of a hand, foot, or arm. As students in Ouro Preto investigated mathematics in their own city, they were surprised to find that a standard measurement was not used when building the houses on the street. The length used—a *barras*—was related to an emperor who standardized the measurement system using his own body parts. In this exercise, students will explore nonstandard English measurements, metric measurements, and their history.

Explore and Create

1. Discuss with students the types of linear measurements they use in their everyday lives. Ask students to distinguish between those measurements needed for large distances, such as their travel from home to school, and smaller ones, such as the size of lead for their pencils.

2. Have students work in pairs to complete the chart in table 3.1 for six other students (if possible, three males and three females).

Table 3.1
Personal measurement chart

	Thumb (knuckle to end)	Hand Width	Forearm (elbow to fingertip)	Span (outstretched arms)	Foot Length
Student F1					
Student F2					
Student F3					
Student M1					
Student M2					
Student M3					
Average					

3. Ask students to compare their lowest, highest, and average numbers both for males and females and as an overall total. Discuss the differences in measurements and who would profit by using either the largest or smallest of the measurements. Which measurement would a cloth merchant want to use for selling cloth? Which would you use to buy a lot for building a house?

4. Based on the student discussion about differences in the measurements, have students research the history of nonstandard measurements and the need for a standard metric system.

5. Have students complete the chart in table 3.2 for comparison of nonstandard and metric measurements.

Table 3.2
Comparison of measurements chart

Unit of Measurement	Body Part Comparison	Comments
Centimeter		
Inch		
Decimeter		
Foot		
Yard		
Meter		

6. Have students develop different nonstandard measurements of their own, and ask them to compare their choices with those previously discussed in table 3.1.

7. By using their measurements in the tables, have students write algebraic statements to express the relationship between metric and nonmetric measurements, such as "2.54 centimeters = 1 inch."

8. Using the established relationships, use ratios to solve equivalency problems, such as the one below:

A measurement of 6 inches would equal how many centimeters?

2.54 cm/1 in = x cm/6 in; therefore, x = 15.24 cm.

Apply and Extend

- Working in pairs, have students measure items in the classroom such as doorways, desk width, chair height, etc., with both standard and nonstandard measurements.

- Through Internet searches, students should examine nonstandard measurements for cultures other than their own and compare their results.

- Have students use graph paper to plot comparable measurements in three colors (yard, meter, *barras,* etc.) on a bar graph.

Summarize and Assess

Discussion Questions

Q Everyone uses nonstandard measurements in situations where a standard measurement tool is not readily available. What are some nonstandard measurements that students have seen people use? Examples might include a grandparent cooking by adding a pinch of salt, or a parent measuring a fence by pacing off stride lengths. Ask students to research other nonstandard measurements by interviewing adults in their lives about those measurements they use in their jobs or everyday activities.

Q Discuss the types of measurements that students have discovered. Which measurement system would be best to use? What are the advantages and disadvantages of each system?

Grades 9–12

Objectives

Students will collect and analyze data and create functions to describe geometric and quantitative results as variables change.

Materials

- Grid paper
- Calculators
- Square chips or similar manipulatives

Standards Met in This Section
Common Core State Standards—Interpreting Functions
Use function notation, evaluate functions for inputs in their domains, and interpret statements that use function notation in terms of a context (F-IF.2, NGA Center and CCSSO 2010, p. 69).
NCTM Standards—Algebra
▲ interpret representations of functions of two variables;
▲ use symbolic algebra to represent and explain mathematical relationships; and
▲ draw reasonable conclusions about a situation being modeled (NCTM 2000, p. 296).

Introduce

Many streets in towns and cities around the world were once muddy or dusty dirt trails. As time passed, these trails were covered with hand-hewn cobblestones that provided a more consistent (and certainly less dirty) surface for travel. In the Brazilian city of Ouro Puerto, one such cobblestoned street, Rua Alvarenga, is now lined with stores and homes. Cities as old as Ouro Puerto frequently have at least a few streets such as this one, where the street's stonework is still visible and is traveled on by vehicles and pedestrians.

In Brazil, where the main language is Portuguese, the word for cobblestones is *paralelepípedos*. These are stones extracted from local quarries that come in a variety of sizes based on their use. Stones in main roads, for instance, receive a lot of pounding from horses, vehicles, and people, and they tend to be larger than those in small streets and entryways. Within the same street, each cobblestone is roughly the same dimension. The stones used to pave the surface of Rua Alvarenga measure roughly 6 inches (15.2 cm) wide, 12 inches (30.4 cm) long, and 6 inches (15.2 cm) thick.

Often the stones were placed in tessellated (checkered) fashion where they were arranged to provide a flat and complete street surface. Stone workers were seemingly not just satisfied to cover the street but often wanted to impart a design that was visually pleasing. By offsetting the stones, the workers not only created a more artistic pattern but also, it turns out, made a design that was better engineered and better built to withstand heavy traffic. In the following activity, students will be asked to statistically analyze the number of stones needed to create a row. They will then use that data to suggest a function that designers could employ to calculate the number of stones required to cover a street with a specific width and length.

Explore and Create

1. Streets come in all widths but often are built to accommodate two vehicles. A typical width for most streets is 15 to 20 feet (4.5 to 6 m). Discuss with your students how streets on Ouro Preto are topped with *paralelepípedos* (cobblestones), each roughly measuring 15.2 centimeters wide and thick and 30.4 centimeters long (see fig. 3.2).

Fig. 3.2. Section of cobblestone street

2. Tell students that they need to use stones to pave a street that is 6 meters wide and 60.96 meters long, and challenge them to determine the number of stones required to complete the work. Point out that pavers leave a gap of 2 to 3 centimeters between each stone (on all sides). After the stones are laid, sand is used to fill the gaps and secure the stones in place.

3. Ask students to work in small groups to discuss how they would make their calculations. Require students to create a representative scaled model of the street and to use the cube manipulatives to "pave" it. Because of the gaps needed, the challenge is not as simple as just laying the stones end to end and side by side. What additional calculations are required?

4. Allow student teams to share their diagrams and models to explain how they achieved their results.

Apply and Extend

- After students have made their calculations, discuss the challenge of having to manually calculate the number of stones needed when paving different widths and lengths of roads.

- Challenge students to write an algorithm that would allow a paver to calculate the number of stones needed to place one row of stones across a street 6 meters wide.

- Now challenge students to write an algorithm that would allow a paver to calculate the number of stones needed to complete the job when the road length is determined. In this situation, suggest the students use the street dimensions of 6 meters wide and 60.96 meters long.

- Lastly, challenge students to create an algorithm that would allow a paver to calculate the number of stones needed for any street width and length.

- Encourage students to share their results.

Summarize and Assess

Discussion Questions

Q In these activities, we have experienced using mathematics to solve problems faced in daily life throughout a community in Brazil. Has this experience caused students to look more at their own community through a mathematical lens? If so, what examples come to mind?

Q If a student were to ask a stone worker if he or she was also a mathematician, the worker would probably say he or she was not. Should people who build and design cities and streets be called mathematicians? Why or why not? What makes their "math" similar or different from the math that students are learning in school?

Featured Consultants for This Chapter

Milton Rosa and Daniel Clark Orey *are professors at the Centro de Educação Aberta e a Distância of the Universidade Federal de Ouro Preto, Brazil. Milton has published many articles, chapter books, and books in Portuguese, Spanish, and English. His areas of research include ethnomathematics, mathematical modeling, curriculum and instruction, educational leadership, and the history of mathematics. Daniel also has an international reputation for his inventive work in ethnomathematics specifically related to outdoor mathematics activities. He frequently conducts workshops for teachers or instruction for students on "math trails" that are walking mathematical investigations of communities.*

4

SOUTHWESTERN UNITED STATES
Navajo Beading and Weaving Patterns

Locations   The Navajo areas of the southwestern United States

66 *To be a traditional Navajo, you believe all things live in harmony with each other, from the heavens down to Mother Earth. Numeracy has always been a part of all existence. From the creation of the Universe to First Man and Woman to the present, sacred number, colors, lights and Holy Beings were part of all creation. Because all things are sacred all have thoughts, creativity, life, and spiritual ways.* 99

—*Clayton Long*

Context

The Navajo Nation reservation encompasses parts of three states: New Mexico, Arizona, and Utah. More than 300,000 Navajo people of one-fourth blood or more live throughout the United States, and about 200,000 of them reside on the Navajo reservation. Navajos are the largest Native American nation in the United States. One of the most striking aspects about the Navajo people is their ability to maintain, for the most part, their language, culture, customs, and spiritual roots.

Many people are familiar with such aspects of Navajo culture as their Code Talkers; their fry bread, basketry, wool rugs, and silver jewelry making; and their living in an area that includes two wonders of the world, Monument Valley and the Grand Canyon. They have long been known for their farming, cattle and sheep ranching, and horsemanship skills. For the Navajo, mathematics has always been, and continues to be, an integral part of life applied in all aspects of daily activities. Clayton Long shares, "Mathematics and life are one for the Navajo people. Our ceremonies, traditional arts and crafts, even the games we play such as our string, stick *(Tsidił),* and shoe games, illustrate our constant use of mathematics shaped by who we are, the Navajo!"

Navajo is an Athabaskan language that is linguistically connected to the majority of other Athabaskan dialects spoken in northwest Canada and Alaska. It is thought that the Dine' (what the Navajo call themselves) have made the American southwest their home ever since the 1400s, after traveling south from their northern homelands. Originally, the Dine' practiced hunting and gathering, but interaction with the Pueblo and later the Mexicans in their new location helped the Dine' learn agricultural and ranching skills that define the culture as it is known today.

Life for the Navajo has always presented political, economic, environmental, and social challenges. From approximately 1840 through the 1860s, armed hostilities existed between the Navajo and the Mexican (and later American) settlers for control over the land and its resources. The tensions spiked in 1864 when Kit Carson and his army led a forced relocation of the Dine' from their traditional lands across 300 miles of desert to an internment camp in Fort Sumner, New Mexico. The march, known historically as the "Navajo Long Walk," resulted in numerous deaths, particularly among the women, children, and the elderly. The U.S. government grossly underestimated what would be needed to house and feed such a large number of people. As a result, the relocation was never successful, and a few years later the Dine' were released and allowed to return home. Federal treaties were negotiated throughout the decades, and today the Navajo Nation includes over 16 million acres.

Today on the "Rez," as it is known by those who live on or around it, life continues to present special obstacles and benefits. Poverty rates exceed the national averages, and such issues as teen pregnancy, school dropout rates, drug and alcohol abuse, and suicide are of great concern. Much needs to improve, but there are some positive developments. Opportunities are expanding for students to pursue advanced degrees using programs offering distance education. Students gain access to world-class education while still living with their communities and families.

Some educational leaders and administrators are working to revitalize the teaching and speaking of the Dine' language and to create a more culturally responsive system of education. Courses, particularly in mathematics and science, are being developed to illustrate culturally relevant connections. The mathematical connections made in this chapter incorporate the traditional arts of Native American beadwork and rug weaving. Many Navajo students either know how to bead, know someone who does, or have a relative who weaves fine Navajo rugs, and they can now better see the purpose of learning. As a result, these students learn to value education, recognize the sacrifices others have made so that they may learn, and realize the obligation and opportunity of learning and teaching in Native ways.

For all the activities in this chapter, students can access the virtual beadwork and rug-weaving tools available in the suite of Culturally Situated Design Tools (CSDT) found at http://csdt.rpi.edu.

Kindergarten–Grade 3

Objectives

Students will explore the Navajo craft of bead working through creating their own paper beadwork strips and then graphing the number and color of beads used in their design. Students will then interpret the graph to describe which colors were most and least frequently used. As an extension, students may use the "Virtual Bead Loom" page on the CSDT web site to create and work with virtual beadwork strips.

Materials

- Grid paper
- Colored pencils or markers
- Ruler or other straightedge

Vocabulary

- Greater than
- Less than
- Sorting
- Classifying
- Interpreting

Standards Met in This Section

Common Core State Standards—Measurement and Data

Draw a picture graph and a bar graph (with single-unit scale) to represent a data set with up to four categories. Solve simple put-together, take-apart, and compare problems using information presented in a bar graph (2.MD.10, National Governors Association Center for Best Practices and Council of Chief State School Officers [NGA Center and CCSSO] 2010, p. 20).

NCTM Standards—Data Analysis and Probability

- sort and classify objects according to their attributes and organize data about the objects; and
- represent data using concrete objects, pictures, and graphs (NCTM 2000, p. 108).

Introduce

Making things of beauty has long been a central occupation of the Navajo. Silverwork, beadwork, and rug weaving result in products that decorate one's body or surroundings. Beauty is an important theme among the Navajo, so much so that they have a phrase—*Hózhóogo Yishááł*—meaning "I walk in beauty, balance, harmony, joy, love, and peace." The Navajo say that when we walk in beauty we live our lives in balance with both the physical and spiritual.

Beadwork can be done on a beading loom and then stitched to leather or fabric, or the beads can be sewn directly onto the clothing items being decorated. The colors and designs used in Native beadwork are highly varied. Typically, bead workers create their own art, sometimes following basic design guidelines held by their culture and community. A bead worker may even "dream" his or her design. The colors and designs used often convey a message that may be known to the bead worker alone. While a group of beadwork artisans may produce items that are similar based on the cultural expectation of their community, each is free to make his or her work unique and individual.

Beadwork provides a hands-on demonstration of math in action and is an effective vehicle for teaching mathematics. There is virtually no mathematical concept appropriate for elementary students that cannot be illustrated using beadwork. The suggestions for using beadwork that follow can be used to enhance your mathematical instruction as you make cultural connections.

Explore and Create

1. Use Google Images or a similar search engine to find images of Native American beadwork to share with your class. Ask students what they notice about the beadwork and what story or message they think the bead worker intended. Find out if any students have seen beadwork, decorated something using beadwork, or know someone who does. If so, have those students share their experiences. If not, discuss with your students how people in different communities decorate what they use and wear.

2. Ask your students if they think a bead worker uses mathematics to create and design. Probe to see if your students can explain examples of how a bead worker counts, measures, designs, locates, explains, and plays. (Note that these activities represent dimensions of universal activities that researchers suggest we all do and that illustrate mathematics.)

3. Pass out a strip of grid paper of a consistent size and shape to each student, and give them access to colored pencils or markers. Ask them to design a beadwork strip using at least four different colors. Students should use their color choices to color in the squares on the grid. Encourage them to create a design using colors that can illustrate a story they find meaningful and that they can share.

4. When students have completed their beadwork strips, ask several of them to share their designs and stories. Using one student's example, determine the number of colors used and write the names of these colors in a series of columns of a simple table, such as table 4.1. As a class, count the number of beads of each color as you sort and then classify the number and color of beads used.

Table 4.1
Sample table of bead colors

Color	Number of Beads
Red	17
Blue	15
Yellow	5
Green	22
White	10

5. Draw a simple graph for the class, such as the one in figure 4.1. Along the vertical axis, determine a scale of the number of beads (a scale of 25, counting from 0 to 25 by 5s, may be sufficient). Along the horizontal line, list the colors. Describe and demonstrate to students how to transfer the data from your chart to the graph to help tell your math story in a more visual way. You can represent each bead as a colored circle, as shown here, or you can create a box graph in each color category.

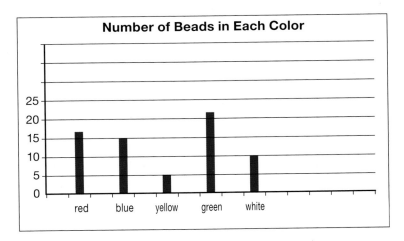

Fig. 4.1. Sample bead-counting graph

6. When the graph is complete, ask the students what the graph is "telling them." What sense are they gaining through an analysis and interpretation of the graph? Ask the students what color was used the most, and the least. How many more (or less) of one color was there than another? Ask students if they can think of any other questions they could pose to the class about the graph and chart. When you have completed your group work, challenge the students to create a graph representing their personal strip and to conduct their own analysis. Students should be expected to create a representative graph and write a sentence or two about what their graph is "telling them." Students should share their graphs and comments in a final summary.

Apply and Extend

- Introduce students to the "Virtual Bead Loom" page at http://csdt.rpi.edu/na/loom/homepage.html, and allow them to explore with the bead-working software. Even very young students will quickly learn to play with variables (ordered pairs) to "drop" beads on the virtual loom. Do not be afraid to allow children to explore, as this is an education in itself. Students often like to pair together and design jointly.

- Encourage students to experiment with the images or designs they create using this technological tool. When students finish what they have made, ask them how they think that math played a part in their ability to make their image or design. Ask them to specifically describe where they see various types of math illustrated in the beadwork. Very young students may say it is in counting or in making shapes. Older elementary students may be surprised to realize that a bead strip can be used as an array model, such as they use when studying multiplication. Challenge students to use this concept to quickly compute the total number of beads in any strip, through multiplying number of beads in a column by the number of rows in the strip.

Summarize and Assess

Discussion Questions

Q This lesson explores how the Navajo culture uses beadwork to illustrate shapes and images valued within their community. What other art work created by other indigenous cultures can you think of where mathematical applications are apparent?

Q Many Navajo believe people must live in balance with all of nature and strive to live their lives so that they "always walk in beauty." During this lesson, we have seen beautiful examples of Navajo art. Do the students think that Navajo craftspeople consider mathematics to be "beautiful"? Do they think so themselves?

Grades 4–8

Objectives

Students will use Native beadwork patterns as the background for reviewing basic geometry knowledge and practicing formal and informal measurements. They will identify ways to measure informally and apply that knowledge to the beadwork designs.

Students will then use grid paper to create their own designs, and they will use ratios and fractions as they complete their patterns and compare the frequency of bead colors used in the designs.

Materials

- Paper
- Pencil
- Grid paper
- Colored pencils
- Calculator
- Various school items such as paper clips, pens, staplers, etc.

Standards Met in This Section
Common Core State Standards—Number and Operations—Fractions
Solve word problems involving addition and subtraction of fractions referring to the same whole and having like denominators, e.g., by using visual fraction models and equations to represent the problem (4.NF.3, NGA Center and CCSSO 2010, p. 30).
Common Core State Standards—Ratios and Proportional Relationships
Use ratio and rate reasoning to solve real-world and mathematical problems, e.g., by reasoning about tables of equivalent ratios, tape diagrams, double number line diagrams, or equations (6.RP.3, NGA Center and CCSSO 2010, p. 42).
NCTM Standards—Number and Operations
▲ work flexibly with fractions, decimals, and percents to solve problems;   ▲ develop and use strategies to estimate the results of rational number computations and judge the reasonableness of the results; and   ▲ develop, analyze, and explain methods for solving problems involving proportions, such as scaling and finding equivalent ratios (NCTM 2000, p. 214).
NCTM Standards—Geometry
▲ identify, compare, and analyze the attributes of two-dimensional shapes and develop vocabulary to describe the attributes; and   ▲ explore congruence and similarity (NCTM 2000, p. 164).
NCTM Standards—Data Analysis and Probability
▲ collect data using observations, surveys, and experiments; and   ▲ formulate questions, design studies, and collect data about a characteristic shared by two populations or different characteristics within one population (NCTM 2000, pp. 176, 248).

Introduce

A practice common to all people is that of decorating everyday objects. The practicality of an object is not enhanced by the creation of a design, but people everywhere seem to share a need for, and a love of, creative designs on their everyday items. Most Native American languages have no word for *art*. The notion of art as a separate idea had no meaning for Native Americans, because they incorporated it as a necessary and expected element into their daily lives.

The process of stringing an elk tooth or a bear claw, or sewing porcupine quills, and later, colorful glass beads, was a joyful event that celebrated life and the individuality of the maker. Patterns are found everywhere in nature. Nature patterns have been copied and adapted by people all through time. Before beads were available, porcupine quills were used as decoration, and their early influence on traditional patterns can still be seen in the beadwork patterns used today. Quills did not lend themselves to covering large areas of embroidery, so short bands of decoration were quilled and then sewn onto the leather surfaces. Common designs included crosses, squares, stripes, rectangles, and triangles.

The Oñate expedition to New Mexico during the late 1500s is recorded as carrying more than 80,000 glass beads to the region. As their value in decorating became known, the beads became highly popular trade items. Later beads were referred to as "pony beads" because of their transport by pony pack trains. The most common colors were white and light blue, with a few dark buff, dark blue, and red beads available.

Explore and Create

1. Provide students with examples of Native beadwork (photos or actual objects) to examine and discuss. Decorated objects such as hat bands, belts, bags, shirts, and dresses will give students an introduction to the designs that are most typical. Discuss the geometry of the beadwork, and ask the students to identify examples and types of geometric figures found within the patterns.

2. After they have examined several patterns, have students use their grid paper to make a frequency chart (similar to table 4.2) and record the types of geometric figures found in the patterns.

Table 4.2
Bead shape frequency chart

Shape	Tally	Frequency
Triangle		
Square		
Rectangle		

Shape	Tally	Frequency
Cross		
Circle		
Other		

3. Have students examine the colors of beads found within one or more of the patterns. If possible, have them compare older patterns with modern examples. How are the patterns and colors different? How could you identify a modern pattern from the colors?

4. After examining patterns for color differences, ask students to make another frequency chart (such as the one in table 4.3) to record the numbers of each color of beads used within one or more patterns. Students should use a section of the pattern that is complete but does not repeat the design elements. Using the entire pattern would result in large numbers that would not add to the purpose of the activity.

Table 4.3
Bead color frequency chart

Color	Tally	Frequency
White		
Black		
Blue		
Red		
Yellow		

5. Use the first frequency chart (the one on shapes) to explore the ratios of the types of geometric figures found within the designs. What is the ratio of triangles to total figures within a pattern? What is the ratio of triangles to other figures within the pattern? Similar questions can be posed about the ratios of the shapes.

6. Using the information from that frequency chart and the ratios of shapes within the pattern, extend the pattern to a larger format. If the pattern is doubled, what happens to the ratios? How many triangles would be included in the doubled pattern?

7. Use the second frequency chart to explore ratios of bead colors. Pose questions such as: What is the ratio of white to blue? White to red? White to total beads?

8. Using the information from the second frequency chart and the ratios of beads, extend the pattern to a longer design. If the pattern is tripled, what happens to the ratios? How many beads of each color would be needed for the increased pattern?

Apply and Extend

- Ask students to use their grid paper to create a beadwork design that can be extended and replicated to make a bookmark that is approximately 12 inches long and $1/2$ to 1 inch wide. Each square represents one bead of the design.

- Students should identify bead colors to be used in their design with colored pencils. Based on their individual creations, they should be able to determine how many beads of each color will be needed to complete the bookmark.

- Suppose you want to make a bookmark that is similar to the original one but only half as large. How many beads would you use? Draw the new design on the grid paper.

- Native bead workers did not use metric or customary measuring tools as they made their designs. What everyday items could you use to estimate the length and width of your bookmark if you did not have access to a ruler? Some examples for students include:

  - Paper clip, $1^1/4$ inches
  - Scotch tape, $1/2$-inch wide
  - Plastic writing pen without the cap, $5^1/2$ inches
  - Sheet of paper, $8^1/2$ inches wide and 11 inches long
  - Floor tiles in room, most commonly 12 inches by 12 inches

Summarize and Assess

Discussion Questions

Q What was most surprising about the beadwork patterns and their geometry designs?

Q How could someone explain the process of creating a design? What suggestions would you give for increasing the design?

Grades 9–12

Objectives

Students will develop algorithms to "ethno-compute" geometric designs to create beadwork and rug weaving patterns.

Materials

- Computer access to the "Navajo Rug Weaver" page at http://csdt.rpi.edu/na/rugweaver/index.html.

Introduce

The Navajo have long been recognized as some of the finest rug weavers in the world. The wool used in the weave comes from the Navajo-Churro sheep, a rare breed introduced to the desert southwest nearly four hundred years ago by Spanish settlers and explorers. The wool of the sheep is perfectly suited for Navajo rug weaving because of its strength and texture. Natural dyes are employed to create dyed wool in a variety of beautiful colors particularly prized by weavers and rug owners alike.

The history of these rare sheep (and therefore the history of Navajo rug weaving itself) includes the near extinction of the breed in the 1860s. At that time, U.S. government soldiers were forcing the Navajo from their lands by killing their herds, cutting down fruit trees, and destroying the corn fields so vital to their existence. Fortunately, some sheep were hidden to avoid their destruction, and this allowed the breed to survive. More recently,

Fig. 4.2. Navajo rug

university researchers and agronomists have worked with Navajo breeders to enlarge the herds to more sustainable numbers.

Navajo creation stories describe one of the many holy beings as "Spider Woman." Spider Woman is honored for teaching the Navajo the art of weaving as a means to illustrate the order and beauty of the universe. Many traditional weavers still create a "spirit line" in their weaving. This is a visible line that runs from an inside pattern to the edge of a rug, typically near a corner. Explanations for the line vary, but most have to do with the idea of allowing the spirit of the weaver to escape the confines of the rug as they pour their heart and soul into making it.

Explore and Create

1. Briefly discuss the history of Navajo culture and rug weaving as depicted in the above section, and ask students what further questions about it they may have. Make a note of the questions posed.

2. Allow students access to the Internet or school library to try to locate information that would answer their questions. Students then should briefly share their discoveries. This building of context helps to situate the mathematical activities to follow, and it also helps students to realize that mathematics is fully integrated in all aspects of life and history.

3. As a group, access the Web and search for online video clips depicting Navajo weavers as they card wool, dye the yarn, set their loom, or weave their rug. Search for images of rugs and discuss the patterns that students see.

4. Discuss with students the concepts of geometric translations, symmetry, and pattern iterations that they notice in the different designs. Many rug patterns have certain names to describe their style. When such names arise, ask your students to explain why they think these names were created.

5. Lastly, have students visit the Navajo Rug Weaver page at http://csdt.rpi.edu/na/ rugweaver/index.html. Teachers may decide to investigate the site with their guidance as a class or else allow students to explore freely. The site and tools are designed to encourage investigation and pique student curiosity. As the tools are explored, students will practice the skill of *ethno-computing*—the study or application of exploring culture through computing. Students will also investigate mathematical and geometrical concepts as they use the computing software to create replicas of rug images.

Apply and Extend

- After students have sufficiently explored using the tools to create image or design replications, they should be encouraged to create new and novel image designs as they create a virtual rug.

- Ask students to explore the scaling and iteration factors that allow them to create things of beauty with this virtual weaving experience. Ask them to note, and discuss with them later, what questions they found themselves asking or what product were they trying to create. Such introspection allows students to become more aware of how thinking shaped through mathematical application can allow them to create beauty. Point out to the students how in a typical math class they may simply be consumers of the mathematics provided them, but now they are the producers of art using a variety of mathematical concepts and current technologies.

Summarize and Assess

Discussion Questions

Q   As students consider their future education and career options, do they believe there will be a growing demand for those who can create new applications in design and manufacturing? Can any of your students see themselves pursuing such a trajectory?

Q   Ethno-computing is an exciting new field illustrating the connections between what cultures and communities create using the most modern of technologies. While the term itself is new, ask your students if they believe the connections themselves are new, or if cultures, math, and technologies have always interacted throughout history. Why or why not?

Featured Consultant for This Chapter

Clayton Long, *a member of the Navajo Nation, sends Yá'a't'ééh (greetings). As the director of bilingual education for Utah's San Juan School District, he works with seven Navajo language teachers throughout the county on developing Navajo language and cultural materials for students. He helped to produce the Rosetta Stone Navajo on CDs and online, and he is currently using the Rosetta Stone Navajo software as part of an online Navajo class for high school students.*

5

GHANA
Adinkra Symbols

Location   The Western African nation of Ghana

66 *Partnering with math teachers and Adinkra artists in Ghana has been a crucial part of my work as a computer science graduate student, as I attempt to create software that can reflect the sophistication and beauty of indigenous knowledge. From developing an algorithm for drawing logarithmic curves to animating the carver's hand, math helps me move between these two worlds of hand-crafted tradition and high-tech computation.* 99

—Bill Babbitt (at left, talking with Adinkra expert Gabriel Boakye)

Context

Adinkra symbols are prevalent throughout Ghana. They are the traditional symbols of the Asante (also known as Ashanti) culture, which developed in the country's central region. Each symbol represents an ideal or belief, along with a proverb held by the Asante people. For instance, the symbol in figure 5.1 is called *Akokonan* ("the leg of a hen"); it represents mercy and nurturing, as it recalls the proverb "The hen steps on her chicks but does not hurt them."

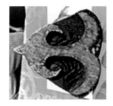

Fig. 5.1. *Akokonan:* "The Leg of a Hen"

61

What we know of the origins of Adinkra is based on Asante oral history. It states that Adinkra has its roots in Gyaman, an African kingdom that began in medieval times and was located in the present country of Ivory Coast (Côte d'Ivoire). At that time, spiritual leaders and royalty wore cloth stamped with the symbols to important ceremonies. In the early nineteenth century, the Gyaman people attempted to copy the Golden Stool, the Asante's symbol of absolute power. In a resulting military conflict, the king of the Gyaman, Nana kofi Adinkra, was killed. Nana Osei Bonsu-Panyin, the *Asantehene* (Asante king), took his opponent's Adinkra cloth as a trophy. With this, the Asante claimed the art of stamping cloth with Adinkra symbols.

Today, the most common use of Adinkra is still in textiles. The Asante use a traditional stamping process to create cloth that is worn to ceremonies and festivals (as shown in fig. 5.2). The colors of the cloth and the symbols it features represent the sentiments of the event. At funerals, for instance, individuals will adorn themselves with black, brown, or brick-colored cloth that is stamped with symbols pertaining to mortality or religion.

Fig. 5.2. Stamped Adinkra cloth

In order to stamp the fabric, symbols are carved into a calabash and attached to bamboo sticks for a grip. Adinkra designers produce their own ink by shaving the bark of a Badie tree *(Bridelia ferruginea),* pounding it, soaking it, and then boiling it. This results in a thick black ink called *Adinkra aduru,* or Adinkra medicine. Cloth is then laid out along a table, and the stamps are dipped in the ink and then pressed down on the cloth an equal distance apart. In Twi (or Akan), the language of the Asante, *Adinkra* translates to "good-bye"; accordingly, cloth stamped with Adinkra symbols was at first often worn to funerals. Over time, the traditions surrounding Adinkra have evolved. Today, symbols can be seen in architecture, sculptures, pottery, and even incorporated in company logos, providing a profound significance to the objects on which they are placed. While the original symbols are still used, new symbols and meanings are constantly being developed.

One of the most interesting aspects of Adinkra design is how the symbols incorporate elements of geometry. Students may enjoy learning how to pronounce the Twi words that represent four possible geometric transformations: *adane* (ah-DAWN-eh) means "reversed image," or reflection; *ketowa* (KET-wah) and *keseye* (ke-SEE-yah) mean "smaller" and "larger" and relate to dilation, which can be a size change in either direction; *ntwaho* (en-TWA-hoe) is the word for "spinning," or rotation; and *twe* (TWEE) is the word for "pulling an object" that relates to translation.

The Adinkra symbol shown in figure 5.3 is called is called *Funtunfunefu Denkyemfunefu* ("the Twin Crocodiles"). It represents democracy and unity in diversity and is based on the proverb "They share one stomach and yet they fight for food." In this symbol, we can see reflection (where one side of the symbol mirrors the other side) along the vertical and horizontal axes.

In *Aya* ("the Fern," shown in fig. 5.4), the leaves gradually become smaller as the fern grows upwards, representing the dilation that can be seen in an actual fern. This symbol represents endurance and resourcefulness. In figure 5.5, we can see rotation in the symbol *Nkontim* ("the hair of the Queen's servant"), which represents service and loyalty. In this symbol, each of the four arms of the spiral are rotated and repeated about a center point.

Translation can be seen in *Ntesie–Mate Masie,* a symbol (fig. 5.6) that represents knowledge and wisdom and is based on the proverb "Deep wisdom comes out of listening and keeping what is heard." Each circle in the symbol is identical to the other but shifted vertically or horizontally to a new position.

Fig. 5.3. *Funtunfunefu Denkyemfunefu:* "The Twin Crocodiles"

Fig. 5.4. *Aya:* "The Fern"

Fig. 5.5. *Nkontim:* "The Hair of the Queen's Servant"

Fig. 5.6. *Ntesie–Mate Masie:* "I have heard it and kept it"

Kindergarten–Grade 3

Objectives

Students will create their own Adinkra stencils. They will use them to explore calculating area using the operations of addition and multiplication.

Materials

- Sheets of colored paper (8 × 10 inches)
- Plastic resealable bags filled with 24 paper squares (2 × 2 inches)
- Glue
- Inch rulers

Standards Met in This Section

Common Core State Standards—Measurement and Data

Measure areas by counting unit squares (square cm, square m, square in, square ft, and improvised units).

Relate area to the operations of multiplication and addition. Find the area of a rectangle with whole-number side lengths by tiling it, and show that the area is the same as would be found by multiplying the side lengths. Multiply side lengths to find areas of rectangles with whole-number side lengths in the context of solving real world and mathematical problems, and represent whole-number products as rectangular areas in mathematical reasoning (3.MD.6 and 7, National Governors Association Center for Best Practices and Council of Chief State School Officers [NGA Center and CCSSO] 2010, p. 25).

NCTM Standards—Measurement

- ▲ explore what happens to measurements of a two-dimensional shape such as its perimeter and area when the shape is changed in some way (NCTM 2000, p. 170).

Introduce

Adinkra symbols are designs created by the Asante people and used to decorate many items of daily use in Ghana. Adinkra cloth is beautifully designed cloth stamped with patterns of symbols, often ones that represent things seen in nature such as trees, ferns, and animals. Each symbol has a specific meaning and a proverb related to it.

Asante artists carve Adinkra stencils from gourds and then use these stencils with hand-made dyes to place patterns on an area of cloth they are designing. You can imagine how much calculation the artist needs to use as he or she decides on the size and shape of the stencil design, where to locate the designs to produce the desired pattern, and how many designs are needed to cover the surface of the cloth they are stenciling.

Explore and Create

1. Show students several photo examples of Adinkra cloth, asking them to pay particular attention to the geometry of the patterns. Explain that each design represents a particular image, object, or idea to the Asante people who produce and wear the cloth. Explain that a proverb (such as those mentioned in this chapter's Context section) accompanies each design and reminds those in the community of an important cultural concept. Discuss proverbs and ask your students what they think several of the Asante proverbs actually mean. Explain that an artist covers or "tiles" an area with a specific design and must know where to place the designs and how many will be needed to cover the cloth as intended. Asante artists are expert at designing and placing patterns across the cloth they decorate so that entire areas become patterned.

2. Divide the students into pairs, and give each pair an 8 × 10-inch sheet of blank colored paper and a plastic bag with 24 white paper squares measuring 2 inches square. Ask students to estimate how many squares will be needed to completely cover the paper's surface. Ask them to then begin placing and gluing the squares so that the entire surface of the colored paper is covered.

3. Discuss with students the concept of area, making sure to focus on the concept of area rather than on the formula for finding an area. How many students counted the squares to determine their answer? Did any students do this differently? Can any students suggest a faster way of calculating area other than by counting? Encourage divergent and flexible thinking.

4. Introduce the terms *length, width, area,* and *perimeter.* Discuss the concept of using a variable to represent a particular term (i.e., l = length or w = width). As students work within their teams and as a whole class, ask them to write a sentence describing how they would tell a friend to find the area of a surface when using a specific dimension. Together, have the class translate these word sentences into a formula they can apply when calculating the areas of differently shaped surfaces.

Apply and Extend

- Refer back to the discussion you had with your students as you guided them to discover a formula for calculating area of a two-dimensional surface. Ask the students what would happen to the previously calculated area if the stencil pieces they were using were now doubled. Have them construct one 4-inch square (4 × 4) with their 2 × 2-inch squares. Note how many of the 2 × 2-inch squares are used. How many 2 × 2-inch squares are needed to make one 4-inch square? When the dimension of a shape is doubled, does this mean that the area also becomes twice as large? If students are asked to increase to triple the dimensions of the original 2 × 2-inch square, what do they predict would happen to the area? What have they discovered?

- Remind the students of the number of 2 × 2-inch squares they previously used to tile their colored paper. Ask them to draw 4-inch squares to tile another sheet of colored paper and compare the number of 4-inch squares needed with the number of 2 × 2-inch squares used. What did they discover? What possible explanation could there be for this result?

Summarize and Assess

Discussion Questions

Q We now have a better understanding of the way that Adinkra artists calculate area and how they determine how many designs will cover an area of cloth. In what other ways do these artists use math?

Grades 4–8

Objectives

Students will explore the presence of transformational geometry—reflection, dilation, rotation, and translation—in indigenous design and, as a result, gain a more thorough understanding of geometry's relationship with nature. They will collaborate in groups to distinguish how the transformations are portrayed in a variety of Adinkra symbols and will then have an opportunity to design their own symbols, incorporating a variety of transformations. Using an online applet, students will graph their design, providing a connection between transformational geometry and coordinate graphing.

Materials

- Web page with "Adinkra Grapher" applet at http://csdt.rpi.edu/african/adinkra/index.html
- Poster board
- Markers
- Notebook paper and pencil
- Graph paper
- Ruler
- Protractor
- Compass

Standards Met in This Section

Common Core State Standards—Geometry

Describe the effect of dilations, translations, rotations, and reflections on two-dimensional figures (8.G.3, NGA Center and CCSSO 2010, p. 56).

NCTM Standards—Geometry

- describe sizes, positions, and orientations of shapes under informal transformations such as flips, turns, slides, and scaling;

- examine the congruence, similarity, and line or rotational symmetry of objects using transformations;

- draw geometric objects with specified properties, such as side lengths or angle measures;

- use visual tools such as networks to represent and solve problems;

- use geometric models to represent and explain numerical and algebraic relationships; and

- recognize and apply geometric ideas and relationships in areas outside the mathematics classroom, such as art, science, and everyday life (NCTM 2000, p. 232).

Introduce

Adinkra symbols are representations of beliefs and values held by the Asante people of Ghana. Many of these designs draw on aspects of nature, and they often incorporate elements of geometric transformations such as reflection, dilation, rotation, and translation. Through a study of these designs, we can gain an understanding of how these transformations embody aspects of the natural world. In this exercise, students will have an opportunity to design a symbol using these transformations, allowing them to creatively portray their own connection with nature.

Explore and Create

1. In pairs, have students navigate to the "Transformational Geometry" page under the Culture section of the web page listed in the Materials list. Have students read through the pages on each transformation, noting how transformational geometry is present in Adinkra symbols.

2. Separate the class into four groups. Assign each group a geometric transformation—reflection, dilation, rotation, or translation. Hand each group a piece of poster board, and instruct the students to create a poster on their geometric transformation. The poster should include a definition of the transformation and at least three examples of Adinkra symbols that incorporate it. (For a collection of Adinkra symbols, navigate to http://www.adinkra.org/htmls/adinkra_index.htm.) For each symbol they choose, have students draw the symbol, write its literal meaning, and write its symbolic meaning.

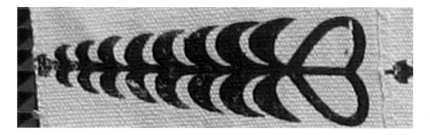

Fig. 5.7. *Aya:* "The Fern"

3. Have the groups present their posters. As each group presents the symbols on their poster, ask the entire class to suggest what element of nature the symbol represents and how the geometric transformation can be seen in that element. For instance, if students were presenting *Aya,* the fern (fig. 5.7), they would describe how the dilation that can be seen in the symbol's leaves depicts the dilation in the leaves of an actual fern.

4. Tell students to think about their own values and possibly identify an element of nature that somehow depicts these values. On sheets of paper, have students incorporate linear shapes and arcs to design their own symbol that depicts these values. Their symbols should also incorporate at least one of the geometric transformations.

5. After they complete their initial sketches, have the students use a ruler, a protractor, and a compass to plot their designs on a piece of graph paper. Have the students record the coordinates for each point of their design on the graph paper. Also have them record the radius and angle of each arc.

6. After plotting their design on graph paper, have students navigate to the "Math Software" section on the Adinkra Grapher web page (as shown in fig. 5.8). Have the students use the applet to plot their symbol.

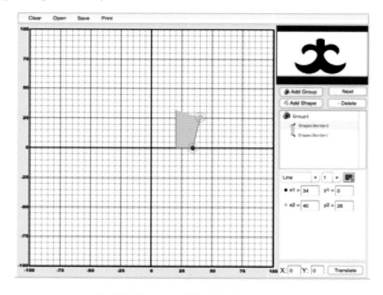

Fig. 5.8. Example of "Math Software" page

Apply and Extend

- Have students print out their designs and share them with the class. Ask students to describe the shapes and arcs within their symbol, along with the elements of transformational geometry that it incorporates. Have students also share the values that their symbol represents and how they created the design to represent those values. If a design is related to an element in nature, have the student describe the connection.

- Have students attempt to recreate their design using the "Programming Software" section on the Adinkra Grapher web page. Ask to students to describe what they had to do differently to plot their design on the graph using programming concepts.

- For homework, ask students to record ten instances of transformational geometry that they see in nature or in their homes. Have students share their findings during the following class.

Summarize and Assess

Discussion Questions

Q Did many of the symbols incorporate more than one element of transformational geometry? Which transformations were often paired, and why do they complement each other?

Q How does knowledge of transformational geometry make it easier to measure and place shapes on the graph? Explain your thinking.

Grades 9–12

Objectives

Students will explore and model scaling factors with arithmetic sequences such as the Fibonacci numbers. They will also model scaling with geometric sequences, such as squaring reflecting examples as found in both nature and African design. Students will use an online applet to study and create Adinkra patterns reflecting designs found in nature and the Asante culture.

Materials

- Web page with "Adinkra Grapher" applet at http://csdt.rpi.edu/african/adinkra/index.html

- Grid paper

- Ruler and protractor

Standards Met in This Section

Common Core State Standards—Modeling

The basic modeling cycle involves (1) identifying variables in the situation and selecting those that represent essential features, (2) formulating a model by creating and selecting geometric, graphical, tabular, algebraic, or statistical representations that describe relationships between the variables, (3) analyzing and performing operations on these relationships to draw conclusions, (4) interpreting the results of the mathematics in terms of the original situation, (5) validating the conclusions by comparing them with the situation, and then either improving the model or, if it is acceptable, (6) reporting on the conclusions and the reasoning behind them (NGA Center and CCSSO 2010, pp. 72–73).

Common Core State Standards—Geometry

Use coordinates to compute perimeters of polygons and areas of triangles and rectangles. (G-GPE.7, NGA Center and CCSSO 2010, p. 70)

Apply geometric methods to solve design problems (e.g., designing an object or structure to satisfy physical constraints or minimize cost; working with typographic grid systems based on ratios) (G-MG.3, NGA Center and CCSSO 2010, p. 78).

NCTM Standards—Geometry

- ▴ use trigonometric relationships to determine lengths and angle measures; and

- ▴ understand and represent translations, reflections, rotations, and dilations of objects in the plane by using sketches, coordinates, vectors, function notation, and matrices (NCTM 2000, p. 308).

Introduce

As part of their cultural practice, the Asante of Ghana often wear cloth stamped with the symbols called Adinkra to ceremonies and festivities. Artisans carve symbols into pattern blocks, which are then coated with a black dye and the pattern is pressed onto the cloth. The patterns denote important images, often illustrating things found in nature that remind the wearer and those who see the cloths of proverbs important in the Asante community.

Many of the shapes in Adinkra symbols are logarithmic spirals. It's easy to see why when you realize that many Adinkra shapes are inspired by nature, and natural processes are often expressed in logarithmic spirals. The first two examples (figs. 5.9 and 5.10) represent a ram's horns and a bird's foot, both the result of growth curves in nature. In the third symbol (fig. 5.11), the bumps down the middle are related to the knuckles on a fist, representing the concept of power. The proverb that inspired it means "Only god has the power of life"—but how do you represent the concept of "life" in general? For the Adinkra artisans, the symbols involving life always use the arc of a logarithmic spiral, as they have generalized that spiral as a geometric abstraction of the essence of biological growth.

Fig. 5.9. *Dwennimmen:* "Ram's horns"

Fig. 5.10. *Akokonon:* "Hen's foot"

Fig. 5.11. *Gye Nayme:* "Except God"

Contemporary scientists who model the development of biological shapes, or "morphogenesis," also use logarithmic spirals. One way to generate those shapes mathematically is with Fibonacci numbers. (As it happens, Leonardo Fibonacci, the medieval Italian mathematician who devised his sequences, was himself educated in northern Africa.) For instance, in modeling a plant's growth we may compare growth at fixed time intervals and by the amount and direction of growth taking place. It is not unusual to find the results of such studies patterned closely to numbers in the Fibonacci sequence or modeling the creation of iterative golden sections. If the growth of an organism generates a curve, then a very simple model can generate a logarithmic spiral. Scaling factors are also apparent in designs where iterative patterns are scaled. When we look at a fern leaf, for example, we see a repetitive shaped pattern that either increases or decreases in size along the length of the leaf. These patterns of nature illustrating mathematical scaling are often incorporated into African design in art and architecture, and they provide a compelling example of the integration between culture, mathematics, and the natural world.

In the following activity, students will use the online applet to create patterns reminiscent of Adinkra patterns. They will study and create scaling factors to produce geometric transformations depicting the interplay between biological patterns and the cultural designs used in a community. Students will begin their exploration of spirals through a review of the Fibonacci numbers and their ratios. Before starting the activity, review with students how to build the sequence of numbers known as the Fibonacci sequence. A sequence with fourteen numbers should give students a good idea of how the sequence is built and sufficient numbers for further exploration (e.g., 1, 1, 2, 3, 5, 8, 13, 21, 34, 55, 89, 144, 233, 377). This review will then lead students to an investigation of scaling factors to include geometric squaring sequences.

Explore and Create

1. Begin with a discussion of Fibonacci sequences. Fibonacci patterns and numbers are found in many places in nature, and they are also often incorporated by cultures into art and design. Biologically, we can frequently see the successive terms of the Fibonacci sequence appearing in plants. As the plant grows from a small center, young buds move away from the populated area of the old buds to a new location where they are free to expand. This forms a spiral that has consecutive Fibonacci numbers such as spirals with counts of 8 and 13.

2. Have students explore the Fibonacci sequence found in some common, and easy to count, examples from nature. Students should begin by counting the spirals formed from lower right to upper left and record their findings in a chart like the one below (table 5.1). Real-life examples or photos may be used for the investigation.

Table 5.1
Counting spirals in nature

Cone flower	21	34
Daisy	21	34
Giant sequoia cone	3	5
Pine cone	5	8
Pineapple	8	13
Sunflower	55	89

3. Students are now familiar with the numbers of the Fibonacci sequence. Have students explore the golden ratio as they find the quotients of successive Fibonacci numbers. Encourage them to look for a pattern as they continue the exploration, and have them consider what number seems to be the limiting value.

Table 5.2
Dividing successive Fibonacci numbers

1/1	1
2/1	2
3/2	1.5
5/3	1.666…
8/5	1.6
13/6	1.625
21/13	1.615384615
34/21	1.619047619

The value of 1.61818... or ($1 + \sqrt{5}/2$, and symbolized by the Greek letter *phi*, is known as the *golden ratio.* This ratio appears over and over again in nature, art, music, and architecture.

4. Using the numbers from the Fibonacci sequence, have students construct a golden rectangle, either using grid paper or a computer application.

5. Have the students draw a rectangle that measures 55 by 89 units. Within this rectangle, have them construct a square that is 55 units on a side. This remaining rectangle is also a golden rectangle, one that measures 55 by 34 units. Repeat the process using squares of 34 units, 21 units, 13 units, and 8 units. Students should use a calculator to verify the ratios made from the Fibonacci numbers.

6. Have students connect the vertices of the squares to form a logarithmic spiral. A spiral is defined as a curve traced by a point that moves around a fixed point from which it continues to move away. Have students compare the logarithmic spiral to the Adinkra designs provided to them. Ask them to determine how many of the designs exhibit the logarithmic spiral and the associated golden rectangle.

7. Students should be able to design their own Adinkra-style designs using the information learned about golden rectangles and logarithmic spirals. An exciting way to do that is to use the Adinkra programming tool at http://community.csdt.rpi.edu/applications/17.

Apply and Extend

- Ask students to examine the following Adinkra design image (fig. 5.12). The design may remind them of a plant they have seen, such as a corn plant that has been laid on the ground.

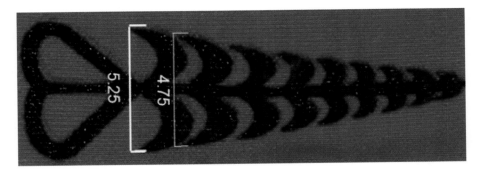

Fig. 5.12. Leaves design

- As indicated, the height of the leftmost set of leaves is 5.25 inches. The height of the next set of leaves (moving to the right) is 4.75 inches. To calculate the scaling factor, the student must divide 4.75/5.25. The resultant scaling ratio is approximately 90 percent. That second set of leaves is therefore 90 percent of the height of the first set. Students should be able to see that there appears to be a constant rate of change as the progressive leaves to the right decrease gradually in height at a scaling factor of .90.

- Ask students to imagine they are artisans carving similar images and are aware of the role of scaling ratios in their designs. Ask them how many leaves should be on an image if they, as the designers, want the last pair of leaves to be no smaller than the tip of a carving chisel, which is 0.25 inches wide. Allow students to explore creating the designs they could make for Adinkra cloth through setting scaling ratios to produce their art.

- Encourage students to explore scaling ratios using the following web page in the suite of Culturally Situated Design Tools: http://csdt.rpi.edu/african/ MANG_DESIGN/culture/mang_homepage.html. They should note the mathematical and physical similarities that connect these designs and artworks with African nature and culture.

Summarize and Assess

Discussion Questions

Q How do cultures incorporate images of their environment, including nature, in their artwork and design? Do you see such connections in your home community? What might it mean if you do or do not?

Q What do you consider to be a key insight that you have gained as a result of your interaction with these mathematical activities?

Featured Consultants for This Chapter

Bill Babbitt *currently has the pleasure of working with colleagues on Culturally Situated Design Tools. The CSDTs offer an opportunity to improve student-learning outcomes by teaching mathematics and computer science concepts through cultural simulations. Additionally, Bill is a co-advisor for Albany Area Math Circle and an assistant coach for the Upstate New York American Regions mathematical League team.*

 **Enoch Bulley** *holds a Bachelor of Science in physics, with an emphasis in electronic/computer-based instruction, from Kwame Nkrumah University of Science and Technology in Kumasi, Ghana. He currently tutors and teaches at Ayeduase Junior High School and serves as the school's Culturally Situated Design Tools representative.*

6

GERMANY
The Game of
Klappenspiel

Locations   Classrooms in Germany

66 *Mathematics is not only the language of science and technology but it really is the bridge that allows us all to understand our world and our place in it.* 99
—*Reiner Kreitner*

Context

As in many countries, schooling is compulsory for all children in Germany, with mathematics a required subject. The German educational mission is designed to provide all children with a quality education, regardless of their nationality, religion, ethnicity, gender, or social rank. As Reiner Kreitner explains:

Elementary schools are considered learning laboratories and living spaces for diverse pupils and should provide our young learners optimal conditions and learning opportunities. Children learn best when what they learn is paired with activities. It is beneficial for students to learn mathematics framed in applications used in modeling real situations and solving real problems.

Reiner Kreitner's work as an engineer demands a high level of mathematical competence, yet he also sees how math is used in every other facet of his life and the lives of those around him. He describes how eager he was to learn mathematics as a child, and how he enjoyed the variety of instructional activities his teachers provided. One activity he fondly remembers is the game of *Klappenspiel* ("shut the box"), which is still used by classroom teachers in Germany today to help students to master their basic addition facts, gain number sense, and investigate and problem-solve.

Reiner's study of Klappenspiel indicates that the game may have been played as early as the nineteenth century in Normandy, and it apparently was particularly popular among sailors.

Later, the game was played in England, where it lives on as a popular entertainment in pubs. In most versions, the game includes a box with nine, ten, or twelve numbered keys. (Fig. 6.1 shows an American version from the Melissa & Doug toy company.) Other versions consist of a sheet of paper or a material that can be written on and wiped clean after each use.

Fig. 6.1. "Shut the Box" *(Klappenspiel)* game

The object of the game is to flip over keys and earn more points than your playing partner. One version of the game has two basic types of moves a player may make. Players can either flip the individual numbers of their roll, or they can flip the sum of those numbers as they alternate turns. Players earn the points they flip. At first, the game appears deceptively simple, requiring only basic calculation and decision making. In reality, it becomes much more complex, as probability and a few extra rules come into play. If a player rolls the dice and cannot flip those two numbers because of the numbers remaining, they lose their turn and their opponent rolls. When neither player can make a flip, that game ends and scores are calculated. If a player throws doubles, then he or she can only play the sum—unless it is a double six, in which case the game also ends and scores are calculated. The winner is the player having the greatest overall sum of scores after a predetermined number of games have been played.

Reiner's sons taught him a version they played in school that encourages even more strategy and calculation. The objective in that variation is for each player to close all doors ("shut the box") while accruing no negative points. This version can be played by two, three, or more players until all but one player reaches a penalty score of 45 or more points (45 is the sum of all nine keys).

This game version also allows the player to flip any two keys whose sum is equal to the original sum rolled. For instance, imagine that a player rolls a 6 and 3. The numbers used can then be any decomposition of the total sum of 9, such as 1 + 8, 2 + 7, 3 + 6, or 4 + 5. When six or fewer keys remain, the player continues his or her move with only one of the two dice. If the player cannot flip a key, his or her turn is lost. If neither player can flip, the game is over. In this alternate version, the sum of numbers not flipped is calculated and considered as a penalty. Players who reach a total of 45 penalty points are eliminated from further play, and the game continues until there is just one surviving player.

Kindergarten–Grade 3

Objectives

Students will master the basic facts of single-digit addition and subtraction. They will use these basic facts to play a game that provides opportunities for creating winning strategies through problem solving while also introducing simple concepts of probability.

Materials

- A Klappenspiel game board, or a paper model or erasable slate of one
- Pairs of regular dice
- Chips or counters for students to model the sums they investigate (optional)

Vocabulary

- Die
- Dice
- Sum
- Data
- Probability

Standards Met in This Section

Common Core State Standards—Number and Operations

Add and subtract within 20, demonstrating fluency for addition and subtraction within 10. Use strategies such as counting on; making ten (e.g., $8 + 6 = 8 + 2 + 4 = 10 + 4 = 14$); decomposing a number leading to a ten (e.g., $13 - 4 = 13 - 3 - 1 = 10 - 1 = 9$); using the relationship between addition and subtraction (e.g., knowing that $8 + 4 = 12$, one knows $12 - 8 = 4$); and creating equivalent but easier or known sums (e.g., adding $6 + 7$ by creating the known equivalent $6 + 6 + 1 = 12 + 1 = 13$) (1.OA.6, National Governors Association Center for Best Practices and Council of Chief State School Officers [NGA Center and CCSSO] 2010, p. 15).

Fluently add and subtract within 20 using mental strategies. By the end of grade 2, know from memory all sums of two one-digit numbers (2.OA.2, NGA Center and CCSSO 2010, p. 19).

NCTM Standards—Number and Operations

- ▲ develop a sense of whole numbers and represent and use them in flexible ways, including relating, composing, and decomposing numbers; and
- ▲ develop and use strategies for whole-number computations, with a focus on addition and subtraction (NCTM 2000, p. 78).

> **Standards Met in This Section** *(continued)*
>
> **NCTM Standards—Data Analysis and Probability**
>
> ▲ propose and justify conclusions and predictions that are based on data and design studies to further investigate the conclusions or predictions (NCTM 2000, p. 176).

Introduce

Klappenspiel is a game used in German elementary classrooms to help children learn basic addition facts as they develop an understanding of the probability of rolling certain numbers. It provides an enjoyable activity for two or more players. A number of versions of the game exist, and it is suggested that students begin playing the game using either the actual two digits rolled or their sum. As students develop more competence, they can investigate the commutative property as they decompose sums to create other appropriate number combinations. For a further challenge, students may investigate the associative property by decomposing sums with three addends.

Explore and Create

1. Discuss with your students the games that they play and how these games incorporate mathematics. Ask students how the culture of their community helps to shape the games they play.

2. Present a six-sided die and discuss the numbers on its faces. Have the students (working in pairs) drop a die 10 times and record the value after each drop. Ask each pair of the students to analyze their findings and to decide if they believe the die is more likely to turn up with a certain number than another. Create a class chart of their collective data, and ask the students if the data support their initial conclusions. Explain that *probability* is the chance that a certain outcome will occur.

3. Ask students working in pairs to investigate the number of addition combinations of two single digits from 1 to 6. Using a pair of dice, ask them what sums they can roll, and have them chart the related number sentence for each sum rolled. Pose related questions, such as the following: Can they roll a sum of one? What is the largest sum they can roll using two dice? How many ways can they roll a sum of four? Do they think that they can find even more number sentences when rolling a sum of eight? Can they make a prediction of the number of addition combinations (remind them there is no zero on a die) for any sum of 2 through 12?

4. Introduce the game of Klappenspiel, as played by young students in Germany. As a class, play a simple version of the game as you explain its objective and rules. As a starting version, after each roll of dice a player can remove either the two individual numbers rolled or else their sum. Remind the students that values left on the board cannot be eliminated and are considered penalty points. The first team to accumulate 45 penalty points loses the round and a new game begins.

5. Pair students and have them play their first game. Students can use counting chips to help illustrate the sums and combinations. They can also arrange their chips in groups of 10 to help them keep track of the number of penalty points.

Apply and Extend

- In successive games, encourage students to draw pictures of dots to represent their rolls and to later write addition sentences for each of their rolls. This will allow them to connect the concrete representations with the pictorial and abstract.

- Allow students to explore the game further by using three dice and a board labeled with numerals 1–18 as they "flip the keys" to eliminate numbers.

- For a further challenge, encourage students to investigate the associative property, this time by decomposing sums as they explore additional addends that combine to equal the sum rolled. In this version, the game is again played until an individual or team reaches a total of 45 penalty points or more.

Summarize and Assess

Discussion Questions

Q Why are some sums easier to roll than others?

Q How does playing the game help to master basic addition facts?

Q Can the class see numbers and their combinations differently now than they did before they learned the game? What have they discovered about number that they had not previously known?

Grades 4–8

Objectives

Students will build on their knowledge of basic number facts and addition/subtraction strategies. Using the game of Klappenspiel, students will practice basic facts and logic skills for winning the game. Basic probability concepts will be reviewed and expanded as they play the game and roll the dice to score points.

Materials

- A Klappenspiel game board, or a paper model or erasable slate of one
- Pairs of six-sided dice

- Grid paper
- Pencil
- Calculator
- Pairs of eight-, ten-, or twelve-sided dice (optional)

Standards Met in This Section

Common Core State Standards—Operations and Algebraic Thinking

Write simple expressions that record calculations with numbers, and interpret numerical expressions without evaluating them. For example, express the calculation "add 8 and 7, then multiply by 2" as 2 × (8 + 7). Recognize that 3 × (18932 + 921) is three times as large as 18932 + 921, without having to calculate the indicated sum or product (5.OA.2, NGA Center and CCSSO 2010, p. 35).

NCTM Standards—Number and Operations

- ▲ recognize equivalent representations for the same number and generate them by decomposing and composing numbers
- ▲ Develop fluency in adding, subtracting, multiplying, and dividing whole numbers (NCTM 2000, p. 148).

NCTM Standards—Data Analysis and Probability

- ▲ Collect data using observations, surveys, and experiments
- ▲ Use conjectures to formulate new questions and plan new studies to answer them
- ▲ Understand and use appropriate terminology to describe complementary and mutually exclusive events (NCTM 2000, pp. 176 and 248).

Introduce

The German game of Klappenspiel (see this chapter's Context section for a full description) can be used to help middle school students review and expand their understanding of number sums, decomposition, and probability. Students can further expand their understanding of commutative and associative properties through the play of the game. The game has many versions, and the rules vary slightly based on the version chosen.

Explore and Create

1. Pair students together to play the game. Review the rules for this particular version.

- **Objective:** To cover as many of the numbers as possible using a board with values 1 through 9.

- **Play:** The highest roll of the dice determines the first player. The first player rolls two dice, adding the sum to find which numbers to "shut"—for example, a roll of 10 could lead to shutting 1 + 9, 7 + 3, 8 + 2, etc. Player One rolls again and makes another decision about numbers to shut based on the roll of the dice. Once numbers have been shut, they cannot be used again. Once a player has covered the highest numbers of 7, 8, and 9, only one die is thrown. Play continues until no combinations match the remaining numbers. Player One adds the uncovered numbers for a total score. Numbers on the board are flipped over and play begins with a full board for Player Two. Play continues for Player Two in the same manner as Player One. When scores are compared, low score wins, or another round begins, and total scores are compared after a set number of rounds.

- If all the numbers are covered during a player's turn, the box is slammed shut and a winner is declared!

- Ask students to think about their sums, and how 7 + 2 and 2 + 7 are different. Introduce or review the idea of the commutative property. If the rules are expanded to include the use of three numbers to make sums, such as 4 + 3 + 2, this will provide an opportunity to discuss the associative property.

Apply and Extend

- Ask students to think about the results of their game play. Which numbers were easiest to flip over? Which numbers were more difficult to flip? Why do they think this happened?

- Introduce the probability notions of mutually exclusive events, non-mutually exclusive events, and complementary events.

- Ask students what strategies they might use to determine the probabilities of rolling particular numbers for the game. Talk about such strategies as listing, tree diagrams, and tables.

- Using their grid paper, students can make a table that shows all possible outcomes of rolling two dice. A filled-in version of such a table should resemble table 6.1.

- Using the information in the table, students can then calculate the probabilities for each of the sums to occur.

- If pairs of eight-, ten-, or twelve-sided dice are available, students can investigate how the game and the combinations of rolls would be different using such dice, as compared to using six-sided ones.

Table 6.1
Possible rolls of two dice

1st Die	2nd Die	Sum	1st Die	2nd Die	Sum
1	1	2	4	1	5
1	2	3	4	2	6
1	3	4	4	3	7
1	4	5	4	4	8
1	5	6	4	5	9
1	6	7	4	6	10
2	1	3	5	1	6
2	2	4	5	2	7
2	3	5	5	3	8
2	4	6	5	4	9
2	5	7	5	5	10
2	6	8	5	6	11
3	1	4	6	1	7
3	2	5	6	2	8
3	3	6	6	3	9
3	4	7	6	4	10
3	5	8	6	5	11
3	6	9	6	6	12

Summarize and Assess

Discussion Questions

Q How will your game strategy change once you know the probabilities for rolling each of the sums 2–12?

Q Is there a strategy for winning the game or is it all chance?

Q How would you explain your strategy for winning the game?

Q How would the game change if you used two eight-sided dice? Ten-sided dice? Twelve-sided dice? How would you calculate the probabilities for the sums?

Grades 9–12

Objectives

Students will use the game of Klappenspiel as a background for further investigation of number theory, subsets of the rational numbers, and a comparison of number combinations. They will use the basic rules of the game to play it and then begin to decompose the sums into subsets of the rational number set. Students will also use basic probability theory to predict future outcomes of large populations based on a theoretical model.

Materials

- A Klappenspiel game board, or a paper model or erasable slate of one
- Pairs of six-sided dice
- Pairs of ten- or twelve-sided dice
- Paper
- Pencil
- Calculator

Standards Met in This Section
Common Core State Standards—Statistics and Probability
Analyze decisions and strategies using probability concepts (S.MD.7, NGA Center and CCSSO 2010, p. 83).
NCTM Standards—Number and Operations
▲ compare and contrast the properties of real number systems; and ▲ use number-theory arguments to justify relationships involving whole numbers (NCTM 2000, p. 290).
NCTM Standards—Data Analysis and Probability
▲ use simulations to explore the variability of sample statistics from a known population and to construct sampling distributions; and ▲ use simulations to construct empirical probability distributions (NCTM 2000, p. 324).

Introduce

Klappenspiel, or "Shut the Box," is a German game that can be used to engage students in basic number theory and the decomposition of numbers into subsets of the rational numbers. As students explore the various sums, and the numbers that compose those sums, they can identify subsets and classifications of numbers used for solutions.

The game can also be used to help students identify basic combinatorics of the sums and to further explore the role of simulations in predicting outcomes of larger population studies.

Explore and Create

1. Using the basic rules of Klappenspiel (as provided in the Context section of this chapter), have students pair off to play the game a few times to become familiar with its outcomes and number frequencies. Begin the play with six-sided die and ask students to record the outcomes of their games.

2. Have students make a combinations chart of all possible outcomes and the total numbers of ways those can occur (see table 6.1 on p. 82 for an example).

3. Have students review the combinations chart and identify the numbers used to form the sums as prime, composite, or neither. When the outcome is 4, the possible sums needed to make the sum are 1 + 3 (one, and one prime); 2 + 2 (both prime); 3 + 1 (one prime and one).

4. What conclusions can students draw from the above identifications? How many of the sums rely on the use of one, the number that is neither prime nor composite, for a solution? How many of the sums use only even numbers? What is the ratio of odd and even numbers for solutions?

5. Students should further explore the possible combinations by graphing the chart as a bar graph. Which sum occurs most often? Which sum occurs least? Figures 6.2, 6.3, and 6.4 are examples of bar charts that could be used to demonstrate various aspects of the data.

6. Have students use the information from the graph they have created to calculate the probabilities of the outcomes.

7. From their calculated probabilities, students can predict the anticipated number of each sum for a series of games played. Ask students to predict the numbers for a hundred rolls of the dice. They can compare the theoretical predictions to their own empirical evidence from playing the game.

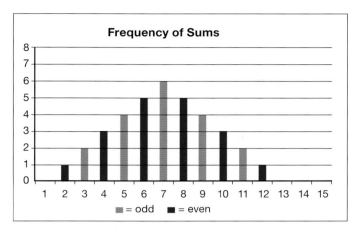

Fig. 6.2. Bar graph of frequency of sums with two dice

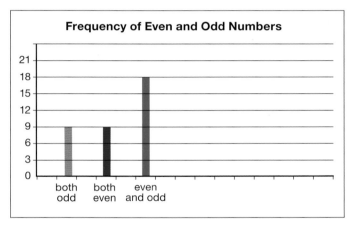

Fig. 6.3. Bar graph of frequency of even and odd combinations of two dice

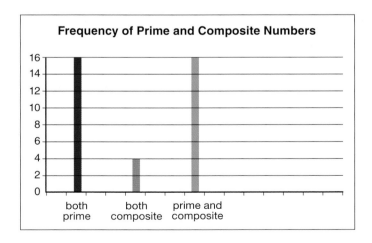

Fig. 6.4. Bar graph of frequency of prime and composite numbers
within combinations of two dice

Apply and Extend

- Have students use a pair of ten- or twelve-sided dice and design their own version of Klappenspiel. How many numbers should be used to play the game? Why would the current listing of numbers, 1 through 12, not be applicable with the ten- or twelve-sided dice?

- Have students make another combination chart with their new sums and the possible numbers used in the outcomes. Compare the numbers with the original chart. What similarities do you see in the two charts?

- Numbers used in the sums can again be identified as prime, composite, or neither.

- One of the unsolved problems in mathematics is that of Goldbach's conjecture. Christian Goldbach (1690–1764) made this guess about prime numbers: "Every even integer greater than 2 can be written as the sum of two prime numbers." For example, 8 = 5 + 3 and 10 = 7 + 3. Some numbers can be written in more than one way, such as 10 = 5 + 5. Have students review their sums and attempt to verify the conjecture.

Summarize and Assess

Discussion Questions

Q How would the possible combinations change if three dice were used in the game?

Q Why are the theoretical probabilities and the empirical evidence different in some instances? How does this affect surveys as the theory is applied to a larger population?

Featured Consultant for This Chapter

Reiner Kreitner *is the quality manager of a German manufacturing company that develops sophisticated high-tech water jet cutting machines that are later manufactured in the United States. Reiner's success depends on his use of mathematics to make statistical analyses and geometrical calculations for the products his company designs. He remembers the delight of his two sons as they learned number calculations and patterns by playing Klappenspiel with his father and two cousins.*

7

URBAN AREAS
Graffiti Shapes and Styles

Locations   Urban areas around the globe

66 *We, as a culture, are obsessed with improving math education, teaching it, and we all wish we were a little better at it. However, we're not spending the critical time talking to each other about what we intend to do with that math or what wonderful things we can create in the world. When working with kids, they're thankfully too honest to do it because they're supposed to. If you can't connect that math education to something that means something to them and gives them room to participate both in the process and in their world, then you're going to lose them.* 99
—*Dan Lyles*

Context

Today, graffiti is generally thought of as words, symbols, or characters permanently and illegally applied to public or private property. It can range from simple scrawls on walls along city streets to elaborate pieces on alleyways or buildings. While graffiti is typically seen in larger urban communities, it can occur anywhere—and often does—in large cities and small towns alike throughout the world.

People have been writing on walls since the dawn of history, and animals the world over leave their scent to mark their territory. Roman soldiers carved their names and created images to indicate "I was here," and these markings are now left as artifacts in the Coliseum. The Ancient Pueblo people of the American Southwest carved petroglyphs and painted pictographs on sandstone walls depicting geometric figures, animals, iconic images tied to seasonal and spiritual rituals, and hunting scenes. Pioneers along the Oregon Trail left their names carved into rocks, as did many other early explorers, cowboys, and soldiers in the American West. Graffiti has been, and probably always will be, a way for people to publicly express themselves. There seems to be an inherent need in all people, of all times, to graphically and physically say "I existed. I was here. This is important to me, so remember it."

Why exactly do people create graffiti? There are many reasons, certainly, but Jacob Barta, a graffiti aficionado (personal communication, April 18, 2012) suggests,

> The purpose of graffiti is fame and notoriety from peers and possibly others. As an entire concept, I would say the purpose of graffiti in general is just letting the world know you are out there. People that lived in caves carved and painted their walls and we have learned from that. You may want to leave your mark in a high-up or far-off place, or a place you may never go to again. I've even been told modern airport workers scribble on the underside of jets.

> The goal of most modern graffiti is attention. People endlessly write the same "name" or "moniker" everywhere they go, and the repetition gets them noticed. Another way to get recognition is to have style—whether it be good, bad, original or not, the way that you write your word will attract attention. If you write your name in a particularly creative way or as big as possible, or somewhere right out in the open, you will probably get positive recognition. If you steal someone's style, cross another name out, or vandalize some place potentially unethical, you will gain negative attention, but all press is good press if you want people to talk about what you have done.

By itself, graffiti is simply the concept of adding a word, name, or picture to a surface where it would normally not belong—the back of a grocery store, a railroad car, wooden fencing, etc.—but there is also a prevailing and popular "scene" in modern graffiti. People tend to write one short word as many times as possible in their city or train yard in order to gain notoriety and a type of fame. There are traditional styles to follow and learn from, and even guidelines and rules as part of a code of conduct. Graffiti as a concept is not required to play out this way, but many people decide to buy in to this scene for the style, history, social aspects, and benefits of becoming better known, or even becoming a graffiti "king" or "queen."

Various forms and styles of graffiti are defined by certain names or lingo. You can have *tagging, scrawling with markers,* or *plain writing* with spray paint. From there, you can move to *hollows* (empty bubble letters), *throws* or *throwies* (filled-in bubble letters), *pieces* (more intricate, often multicolored graffiti efforts), and *burners* (really good pieces). *Blockbusters* or *productions,* which represent the very best, are extremely complicated and very well done.

Lingo is also used to describe style and location. For instance, graffiti in high-up places is *in the heavens.* Graffiti on subways or freight trains is usually fairly clear or easy to decipher in order for the most people possible to see and identify the word or character used, since it is usually moving and far away. More complicated graffiti—or *wild style*—often originates from sketching in *black books* or artist sketchpads, after which it is applied in places that are safe for spending a lot of time.

Graffiti and the images and messages it conveys can be very controversial. People want to communicate with others, connect with others, and share their art. People can use graffiti to change the appearance of their surroundings, which may include the alteration, or seizure, or even the destruction of private property. Jacob Barta questions:

> Why does graffiti get a bad name and yet public billboards are not considered graffiti? They act in a similar manner—everyone has to see them, they promote or communicate a message

or picture you may not support or even go for, they may say something you don't agree with, or be placed somewhere visually undesirable. The difference is that billboards are paid for and legal, no matter what they may say or promote. One may argue that anyone could simply buy their own billboard, but from the stories I have heard that doesn't necessarily fly with communications companies or the cities and states the billboards are in.

Ultimately, graffiti, like beauty, may be in the eye of the beholder. Graffiti may benefit society as a way to beautify public or private spaces, allow people to express themselves, communicate information, and pass along history. It can be a form of political or social protest while allowing people to reanalyze the concepts of space and appearance throughout the world. On the other hand, some think graffiti defaces public or private space and may promote disrespect for property, private or otherwise. Whatever you may think, graffiti is a topic sure to provoke a lively discussion.

Kindergarten–Grade 3

Objectives

Students will identify geometric shapes and correctly name them. They will collect data on the frequency of similar shapes (including whether they are two- or three-dimensional) found in graffiti representing a specific artist.

Materials

- Colored pencils
- Rulers
- Scissors
- Construction paper
- Glue sticks

Standards Met in This Section

Common Core State Standards—Geometry

- ▲ Describe objects in the environment using names of shapes, and describe the relative positions of these objects using terms such as above, below, beside, in front of, behind, and next to.

- ▲ Correctly name shapes regardless of their orientations or overall size.

- ▲ Identify shapes as two-dimensional (lying in a plane, "flat") or three-dimensional ("solid") (K.G.1–3, National Governors Association Center for Best Practices and Council of Chief State School Officers [NGA Center and CCSSO] 2010, p. 12).

Introduce

Famous people are often identified by the music they make, the inventions they develop, or the leadership they provide. How many students have ever considered that some people, namely artists, can be identified by the geometry they use? It's true—some graffiti artists are known for creating their art through a blend of similar shapes that they vary in size, location within the art, and color.

The early art of the graffiti artist named Push relied on the use of a particular geometric shape almost exclusively. When we study his later work, it is evident that he then preferred a different shape and that geometry played a significant role in his art. In this activity, students will study illustrations created by the artist Push. They will measure several of the shapes used in the artwork and recreate a congruent model with construction paper. Students will then create their own art by pasting these paper shapes on a larger sheet of paper. They will complete their artworks by drawing in additional similar shapes.

Explore and Create

1. Review the names of geometric shapes found in real life with the students—squares, rectangles, lines (straight and curved), triangles, and circles. Show students the illustration by the artist Push in figure 7.1, and ask them to touch and name the shapes they see. The majority of the shapes have four sides and therefore are either square or rectangular. Explain that Push in his early days apparently loved to use these four-sided shapes in his work because almost all of his work included them.

Fig. 7.1. Geometric graffiti by Push

2. Introduce the terms *similarity* and *congruence.* Ask the students to identify shapes in the image that are similar. Can they detect any that are congruent?

3. Ask students to study the particular segment of graffiti shown in figure 7.2. Direct their attention to the six-sided figures (irregular hexagons), and ask students to explain what they notice. Do they believe the figures are similar? Are they congruent? Guide the discussion so that attention is paid to common characteristics of the two congruent figures. Discuss the numbers of sides, orientation of shapes, and measurements of interior angles within the shapes. Explain to students the concept of *scaling,* which is what Push uses in his work when similar shapes are repeated but drawn at a different size.

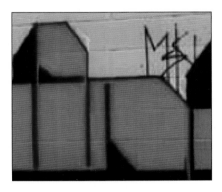

Fig. 7.2. Section of previous graffiti by Push

4. Show students a second illustration of art by Push, one that was done later in his career (fig. 7.3). What do they notice as being similar, and what do they see as being different? Some students may report that the selections of colors were different, and they would be correct. What is probably most striking to most, however, is that in the later work the use of triangles became much more frequent. Divide the students in the class into two groups, one that will recreate an artistic rendition of Push's earlier work while the other creates art similar to his later work.

Fig. 7.3. Later work of graffiti art by Push

5. Provide the materials in the list above. Each student should have their own larger piece of paper upon which to glue the shapes they will cut out and also the ones they will later draw on. Ask students to once again examine the illustration they will use as a model and to measure and cut out at least four shapes they see in Push's example. The pieces need not be measured to be exactly the same size as those in the illustration. Students can benefit and learn if allowed to create their own size approximations.

6. Students should then paste the shapes in the general locations seen in the Push illustration. Some students may select shapes and paste them in positions that leave gaps in their unfinished work. This is to be expected, and students should be directed to draw in and color the missing shapes if they want. After the students have completed their artworks, and before they are displayed around the class, ask them to write a short description on the back of their paper that describes how Push the artist uses math in what he makes.

Apply and Extend

- Many students may wish to explore defining their own style of art by the shapes they choose to use, so allow for this exploration and creativity. The students can cut shapes or draw the figures. Either activity provides kinesthetic effort and helps students feel the sides of the shapes or the sharpness of corners (angles) as they count them. Each student should create their own work of art, or if several students prefer to work together, they can do that also.

- After the art is completed, show the students how to draw and label a T-chart for collecting and analyzing data. The number of different shapes they used in their own graffiti work determines the number of columns they need for their chart. Figure 7.4 is an example of a chart showing how often the artist used circles, squares, and triangles.

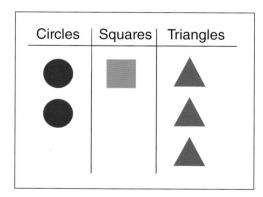

Fig. 7.4. Shapes chart

- Students can complete a picture graph by drawing the number of each kind of shape in the appropriate column. When they are finished, ask the students to write a short description of their artistic style, relating it to the kind, color, and number of shapes they have used.

- Students may wish to study art illustrations from other graffiti artists and try to explain their style using the new geometric lens they have just applied.

Summarize and Assess

Discussion Questions

Q This kind of activity can help to increase a person's ability to notice geometric shapes in his or her world. Pose the following questions: "Is everything in the world comprised of one or more geometric shapes? And if so, is there one shape that we see most frequently both indoors and outside?"

Q If you could choose to be a particular shape, which one would you be and why?

Grades 4–8

Objectives

Students will use the context of graffiti to explore concepts of congruence and similarity. They will find the areas of irregular polygons by decomposing those figures into triangles and using area formulas for triangles. Students will then use this information and apply it to solving real-world problems.

Materials

- Grid paper
- Pencils
- Colored pencils
- Rulers
- Paper
- Calculators

Standards Met in This Section

Common Core State Standards—Geometry

Find the area of right triangles, other triangles, special quadrilaterals, and polygons by composing into rectangles or decomposing into triangles and other shapes; apply these techniques in the context of solving real-world and mathematical problems (6.G.1, NGA Center and CCSSO 2010, p. 44).

Standards Met in This Section *(continued)*
NCTM Standards—Geometry *(continued)*
▲ Precisely describe, classify, and understand relationships among types of two-dimensional objects using their defining properties.
▲ Understand the relationships among the angles, side lengths, perimeters, and areas of similar objects.
▲ Use coordinate geometry to represent and examine the properties of geometric shapes.
▲ Use coordinate geometry to examine special geometric shapes, such as regular polygons or those with pairs of parallel or perpendicular sides (NCTM 2000, p. 232).
NCTM Standards—Algebra
▲ Represent, analyze, and generalize a variety of patterns with tables, graphs, words, and when possible, symbolic rules.
▲ Develop an initial understanding of different uses of variables.
▲ Use symbolic algebra to represent situations and to solve problems, especially those that involve linear relationships (NCTM 2000, p. 222).
NCTM Standards—Measurement
▲ Develop and use formulas to determine the area of triangles, parallelograms, trapezoids, and circles, and develop strategies to find the area of more complex shapes.
▲ Solve problems involving scale factors, using ratio and proportion (NCTM 2000, p. 240).

Introduce

Today graffiti art is practiced by people of all ages and from all around the world. Different styles and complexities of art exist for people who tag: from beginning youth using "bubble letters" to professional writers who continue to develop new styles into adulthood and who are even commissioned and paid by arts organizations or community development groups.

Different communities of graffiti writers focus on their own preferred guidelines for their painting. Some demand freehand writing, while others are focused more on carefully creating art in notebooks and then duplicating it on walls. Some writers collaborate on large-scale murals and create narrative images, often focused on issues of social justice. Some of the diversity of the graffiti also includes referencing other kinds of graffiti. Because of this, it can be very important that graffiti writers spend time learning about styles that they want to imitate or elaborate upon.

Graffiti is multicultural: New York "wild style," for example, represents the ethnic diversity of New York, the city that spawned it. However, many different forms of graffiti have developed around the world, and the rise of Internet communication has allowed groups all over the world to bring local styles into conversation with one another. As the international community of writers grows and diversifies, some have suggested that we use the term "street art" instead of graffiti to include commissioned and noncommissioned forms of mural art from around the world.

Explore and Create

1. Provide examples of graffiti and other outdoor art (such as the one in fig. 7.5 created by the Amsterdam artists known as Graphic Surgery) for students to examine and classify their basic geometric shapes. Each student should have a copy of the graffiti that is large enough for him or her to draw lines and shapes on and make notes on about their discoveries.

Fig. 7.5. Graffiti art example

2. Ask students to look at the designs provided to them and to imagine the entire design placed within a polygonal boundary that just fits the design. What would be the shape of the boundary? Is it a regular or irregular polygon? Review the definitions of polygons and how the measures of sides and angles define polygons.

3. After students have discussed their conjectures about the polygonal boundary, ask them to use their rulers and the graffiti design to draw the polygon about the design. Discuss with students what their containers now look like, the types of angles and lengths of sides used in the polygon, and its classification.

4. Now ask students to work within the polygonal boundary shape. Each of the letters written in the graffiti can be decomposed into triangles and quadrilaterals. Use one letter as a class example and show how a straightedge can be used to draw lines for the decomposition of the letter. By decomposing the area of the letter, triangle area formulas can be used to find the total area of the figure.

5. Students should be given time to work on the design and use their straightedges to decompose the letters into triangles and quadrilaterals. After they have finished the task, discuss what they found as they drew in the straight lines. What types of quadrilaterals and triangles did they find? Were there any patterns that they observed as they began to form the new polygons?

6. If the students need additional practice in viewing the whole as decomposition parts, provide another example and time for them to repeat the exercise with a new figure.

7. Now that the students have begun to look at the graffiti design as a finite set of polygons within a larger polygon, have them use the information to create their own graffiti design. Using a set of parameters—such as size of design, width and length, and the number of letters, limited to four in the first design—have students use their grid paper to make their own graffiti. They should also provide information about the types of polygons used and the number of each.

8. You might ask students to provide information about the polygons they used in a frequency chart (such as table 7.1) so that they can compare individual and class results.

Table 7.1
Frequency chart

Polygon	Number
Quadrilateral	
• Irregular	
• Square	
• Rhombus	
• Rectangle	
• Parallelogram	
• Kite	
• Trapezoid	
Triangle	
• Right	
• Acute	
• Obtuse	
• Scalene	
• Isosceles	
• Equilateral	

9. The classification of the polygons in the designs will give an opportunity to further discuss the properties of the different triangles and quadrilaterals, how they are related, and if any of them fit into more than one of the categories.

10. After students have completed the project, they may wish to enhance the design by using colored pencils to accent the letter outlines and color the letters themselves.

11. Students may then be given the additional assignment of creating a second design with no restriction on the number of letters. They may choose to design their own name, the school mascot, etc., on the grid paper.

Apply and Extend

- Students can use their designs and the decomposition into triangles and quadrilaterals to investigate a real-world application. If the design were to be transferred to a larger area (such as a building wall, a fence, or a billboard), what would be the cost associated with painting the graffiti?

- Ask students to use their geometry skills for scaling factors as they think about placing the design onto a larger area. If each square on the grid paper is one centimeter, what is the scale factor for a design to cover an area of several feet? Students could measure a wall in the classroom or similar area to determine how large the design should be. The use of ratio and proportions can be reviewed and expanded as students determine the measurements needed to make a similar design on a larger design area.

- Students can investigate the amount of paint needed to cover an area. They have the design decomposed into triangles and quadrilaterals. They now also have the scale factor to determine how large the increased polygons would be. By using the area formulas for these geometric figures, they can find the total area for the design.

- Brands of paint differ in the amount of coverage and the initial cost of the paint. Students can use the Internet to research the types of paint available and make a decision based on the cost calculation. If they are given a contract to paint the design, what should they charge? Algebra symbols and equations can be used to model their cost per square foot, fixed costs, and projected revenue.

Summarize and Assess

Discussion Questions

Q Can you find graffiti examples in your own neighborhood? Where did you find the examples?

Q Can these examples be decomposed into the same geometric forms that the students in the class have used in their own designs? How are they different from the ones they designed?

97

Grades 9–12

Objectives

Students will use the online applet at the "Graffiti Grapher" web page to create a graffiti design. They will explore the use of polar coordinates to create arcs of circles, arcs of linear (Archimedean) spirals, and arcs of logarithmic spirals that simulate graffiti geometric forms. For this, they will use either existing examples (such as fig. 7.6) or their own creative designs. Students will also use protractors to measure the slope of a log-linear graph to determine the exponent for a logarithmic curve.

Materials

- "Graffiti Grapher" web page with applet (http://csdt.rpi.edu/subcult/grafitti/index.html)
- Graph paper
- Notebook paper and pencil
- Calculator
- Protractor

Fig. 7.6. "Gusto," New York City, 2006

Standards Met in This Section

Common Core State Standards—Measurement

▲ Apply geometric methods to solve design problems (e.g., designing an object or structure to satisfy physical constraints or minimize cost; working with typographic grid systems based on ratios (G.MG.3, NGA Center and CCSSO 2010, p. 78).

Introduce

Graffiti, if defined as any type of writing on a wall, goes back at least to ancient Rome; if drawn images count, we could even point to the first cave paintings. But the style of urban graffiti that has become an art form traces its history in the United States to large cities during the 1960 and 1970s. Graffiti artists (or "writers," as they prefer to call themselves) are passionate, skilled, community oriented, and socially conscious in ways that profoundly contradict the common portrayal of them as criminals or vandals.

Although the particular city where graffiti was born is disputed, the origin story for graffiti in New York City is well documented. In the late 1960s, a youth who identified himself as "Taki 183" (he lived on 183rd Street in Manhattan's Washington Heights neighborhood) worked as a messenger who traveled all throughout the city. He would use a marker and write his name wherever he went, particularly at subway stations and on subway cars. Eventually, he became known throughout the city as a mysterious figure. In 1971, the *New York Times* interviewed him for an article. When kids all over New York realized the fame and notoriety that could be gained from "tagging" their names on subway cars, they began to emulate Taki 183. The goal was to "get up" (develop your reputation, in the slang of the day) and have your name in as many places as possible. As kids competed with one another to get famous, the amount of graffiti on trains exploded in variety and sophistication.

Explore and Create

1. In the menu on the "Graffiti Grapher" web page (http://csdt.rpi.edu/subcult/grafitti/index.html), you will see a "Culture" section, a "Tutorial" section, and two applets: "Math Software," which uses numeric parameters only, and "Programming Software," which allows students to create their own algorithms. We recommend starting with the Culture section of the website. Divide students into groups, and have each group look over one or more of the sections on graffiti's cultural background. Then have each group report to the class on what they discovered about the history of graffiti.

2. Have students explore the Tutorial section of the website, which will introduce polar coordinates as a natural outcome of drawing on a wall. In the tutorial's "Arcs and Spirals" page, it will do this using the animation shown in figure 7.7.

Fig. 7.7. Animation of drawing an arc on a wall

Here students can see how the shoulder acts as the origin point for the radius of an arc. If the distance between the hand and shoulder does not change, there is a constant radius, and thus you draw the arc of a circle. But if you consistently move your elbow so that you add a little radius with each degree of rotation, you produce the arc of a linear spiral. For example, if we add 0.5 units of length for every degree ($d = 0.5$), over a 124-degree sweep we will add 62 additional units of length, as the distance covered increases from 70 to 132 (see fig. 7.8).

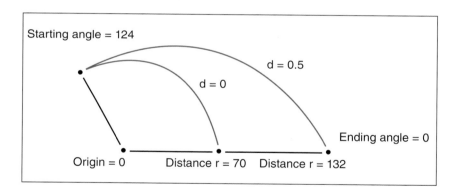

Fig. 7.8. Graph showing arm movements as circular and as a linear spiral

Note that rather than add a constant to the radius for each degree, we can multiply by a scaling factor, producing the arc of a logarithmic spiral. Using combinations of these three simple curves—arc of a circle, arc of a linear spiral, and arc of a logarithmic spiral—students can simulate many of the complex curves from graffiti artwork.

3. Now move to the "Math Software" applet. Students can simulate the graffiti samples on the web page or design their own. Here is one simulation example:

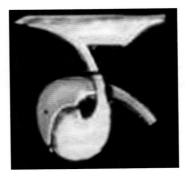

Fig. 7.9. Graffiti simulation example

Using the "Gusto" artwork shown in figure 7.6, we've used a little Photoshop magic to isolate one group of shapes from the upper left, as shown in figure 7.9. We can roughly simulate that group in four steps, using a trial-and-error approach with the software:

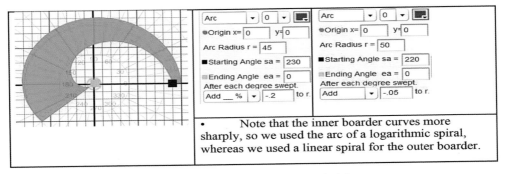

Fig. 7.10. Computer graphing example (*a*)

(*a*) Note that in figure 7.10 the inner border curves more sharply, so we used the arc of a logarithmic spiral, while using a linear spiral for the outer border.

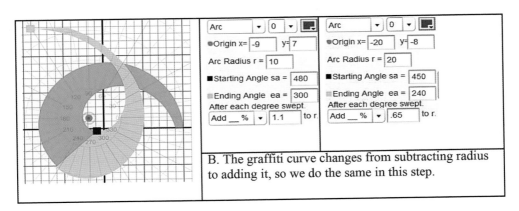

Fig. 7.11. Computer graphing example (*b*)

101

(*b*) The graffiti curve changes from subtracting radius to adding it in figure 7.11, and so we do the same in this step.

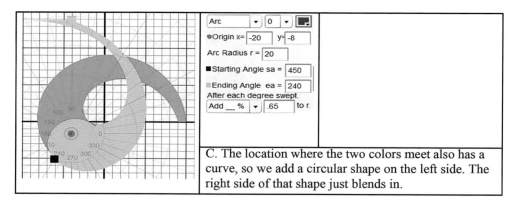

Fig. 7.12. Computer graphing example (*c*)

(*c*) The location where the two colors meet also has a curve in figure 7.12, so we add a circular shape on the left side. The right side of that shape just blends in.

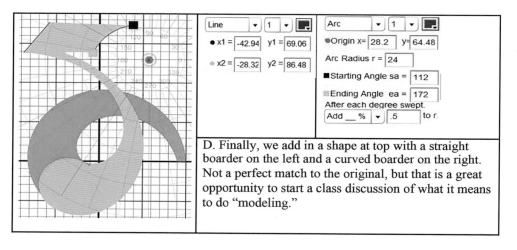

Fig. 7.13. Computer graphing example (*d*)

(*d*) Finally, in figure 7.13, we add in a shape at top with a straight border on the left and a curved border on the right. This is not a perfect match to the original, but it provides a great opportunity to start a class discussion of what it means to do "modeling."

4. Students can also use measurement of graffiti curves to determine the values of the curves. In the example shown in figures 7.14 through 7.16 below, we measure the exponent for the arc of a logarithmic spiral. (For other examples to use, the website www.graffiti.org offers a wide variety of graffiti images from all over the world.)

Fig. 7.14. "Shiva": Hindu-inspired graffiti

Fig. 7.15. Selecting and isolating a curve to investigate

The next step is to actually measure the radius at selected angles of theta. Note that we have flipped the image upside down to make this easier to do. We have provided the protractor here, so students will only need a ruler.

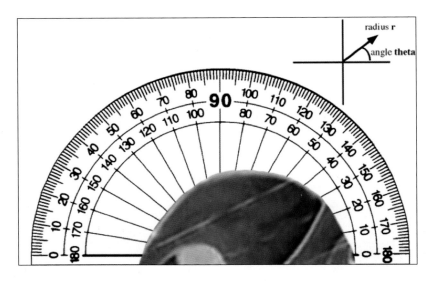

Fig. 7.16. Protractor and curve

Plotting the increase of radius with increasing theta will produce a curved graph. To change this into a linear graph we need to use the logarithmic function: $y = a^x$ expressed as $\log y = x \cdot \log a$. The logarithmic spiral $r = k^{\text{theta}}$ becomes $\log r = \text{theta} \cdot \log k$. Putting this into the form for a linear graph, $y = m \cdot x + b$, we have $y = \log r$, $x = \text{theta}$, $m = \log k$, and $b = 0$. So all we have to do is measure the slope m of a plot of theta versus $\log r$. Since $m = \log k$, then $k = 10^m$. In practice, students can either use log-linear graph paper, or simply calculate the value for the log of the radius and plot it on linear graph paper.

theta	0	10	20	30	40	50	60	70	80	90	100	110	120	130	140	150	160	170	180
radius																			
log radius																			

Fig. 7.17. Radius chart

If students plot the arc of a logarithmic spiral using this value for k, it should closely match the curvature of the graffiti curve. They can test their solution visually by plugging these values into a graphing calculator or online applet; a particularly appropriate choice would be the graffiti curve simulation tool at http://community.csdt.rpi.edu/applications/21.

Apply and Extend

- The task of "curve-fitting" real-world data to a mathematical model is an enormous area within professional applied mathematics and typically involves statistical measures to quantify "goodness of fit." Students can use least-squares regression on the above data and then examine how this can be improved with better sampling methods. Students could be encouraged to seek different types of art beyond graffiti pieces—such as the work below by cartoonist, designer, and graphic novelist John Jennings—and to learn how to model a rougher curve simply by sampling larger areas (fig. 7.18):

Fig. 7.18. Analyzing a curve in a work by John Jennings

Summarize and Assess

Discussion Questions

Q Solving differential equations such as the damped sinusoid above can be challenging, and obviously few if any graffiti artists are using a numeric approach. But as we saw in the case of arcs of spirals—expanding the shoulder-to-hand distance as a function of rotation—these mathematical forms can be associated with the artistic activity itself. How would you describe the arm motion for a damped sinusoid using similar modeling?

Q Many graffiti forms suggest the movement of fluids. How is mathematics used to describe drops of liquid, vortices of turbulence, or other fluid dynamics?

Q Other graffiti forms, such as "bubble letters," suggest stretching. Compare two mathematical models for this phenomenon:

(*a*) Stretching of rubber sheets: a classic way of thinking about topology.

(*b*) Finite element modeling: simulating shapes such as expanding balloons by approximating them as a mesh of vertices linked by springs.

Q How could we explain the relation between the low-income circumstances of many graffiti artists, and the sophisticated geometric forms that they create?

For further reading on this question, see the following books:

Castleman, Craig. *Getting Up: Subway Graffiti in New York.* Cambridge, Mass.: MIT Press, 1984.

McCormick, Carlo, Marc Schiller, Sara Schiller, and Ethel Seno. *Trespass: A History of Uncommissioned Urban Art.* New York: Taschen, 2010.

Featured Consultant for This Chapter

Dan Lyles *is a Texas native who, throughout his life, has participated in various social justice advocacy efforts. In 2010, he obtained his undergraduate degree in sociology from St. Edward's University, and he is a National Science Foundation GK-12 fellow and a MS/PhD student in the science and technology studies department at Rensselaer Polytechnic Institute in Troy, New York.*

8

SOUTH PACIFIC ISLANDS
Stick Charts and Woven Fronds

Locations   Island communities across the east-central Pacific Ocean

66 *In the Pacific, there is a great mix of island cultures—that's what makes the region one of the most interesting to work in. There are mathematical ideas that are specific to an island, but those ideas are sometimes contradictory to the U.S. textbooks that are being used in the schools. The island math is often much more interesting!* 99

—*Barbara Dougherty*

Context

Stretching across the east-central Pacific Ocean are numerous islands that people have called home for thousands of years. The "Islanders" or "People of Oceania" are among the terms used to describe these indigenous inhabitants whose cultures, language, and traditions have been shaped by the environments they have inhabited for so long.

It is thought to be several millennia ago when the first of these peoples migrated in waves from southeastern Asia to reach some of the estimated 20,000 to 30,000 Pacific islands. Today, Oceania is divided into the three geographically diverse areas of Polynesia, Melanesia, and Micronesia. The Hawaiian islands are located in the northern part of Polynesia, the easternmost and largest of the three areas.

The island communities of the South Pacific encompass a great diversity of cultures, but they also share a number of customs and practices. A reliance on the sea is obvious, as fish and shellfish are essential harvests. Oceangoing boat builders demonstrated their knowledge of materials and craftsmanship to build boats and canoes capable of long travel while carrying both people and needed supplies. Using their vast knowledge of the stars, voyagers created

107

"stick charts" and other maps of the seas and islands. Ancient expert navigators employed these—as well as their understanding of ocean currents, wave forms, bird flying routes, and weather patterns—to traverse and explore over three million square miles of sea.

Tropical fruits and vegetables helped to provide for the Islanders' nutritional needs. Other plant materials found in abundance on the islands—such as native grasses, wood from palms and other types of trees, and leaves—were used to create many items for daily uses such as clothing, building homes, fishing, hunting, and defense. One of the more important plants has been that of the coconut palm.

Humans living in tropical regions have found the fronds of coconut trees useful in creating shelter, clothing, and everyday household objects. Weaving the fronds of plants indigenous to the Pacific Islands provided the Islanders with items ranging from mats to hats to even sails for their outrigger canoes. Coconut fronds are durable and easy to bend, making them a perfect choice for weaving beautiful patterns into everyday items. The use of the fronds involves extensive preparation and planning before the creation of the object and the pattern woven into it.

Lauhala refers to the leaves of the hala tree (*lau* is the Hawaiian word for "leaf"). This tree is of great importance to the Pacific Islanders for cultural, health, and economic reasons. Hala leaves are used in weaving items such as baskets, mats, and hats; the patterns employed are often handed down from generation to generation. Houses were fashioned from *lauhala,* including the thatched walls, roof lining, window shutters, mats to cover the floors, and storage containers for household goods. Remains of *lauhala* from burial sites in Hawaii include many of the same patterns that are used today.

This ancient and once common craft has seen a renaissance as artists race to recover what was nearly a lost art (see fig. 8.1). It is not just collectors or tourists who value such woven items, but also the Islanders whose culture these items represent. Indeed, the South Pacific region presents an optimal opportunity for exploring how mathematics is shaped by those who use it, while at the same time mathematics reciprocally helps to shape the cultural communities who use it to survive and succeed.

Fig. 8.1. A craft artist cutting a leaf into lauhala strips

Today we are witness to a growing movement to strengthen traditional Pacific Islander cultures and ensure that indigenous languages and customs are not lost and forgotten. It has not been easy, as modernization—with its promise of higher paying jobs, material luxuries and numerous other enticements—has negatively impacted the organization and peopling of traditional cultural communities. Schools are striving to develop "language nests" where indigenous languages are taught and practiced. Culturally responsive curriculum is being developed and used in schools to help students learn important mathematical, scientific, social, and historical knowledge, all illustrated in contexts that reflect local values, traditions, and customs. Students are beginning to understand their obligation to learn well in order to improve conditions not only for themselves, but for their communities and neighbors as well. Much of this cultural renewal has resulted from community elders helping the new generations learn how Pacific Islander values and customs form a strong foundation for successful learning and development.

Kindergarten–Grade 3

Objectives

Students will explore geometric concepts related to calculating perimeters and areas as they construct stick chart models to create maps of places where they live and play.

Materials

- Plastic straws, or bamboo barbeque skewers with sharp points removed
- Shells, pebbles, seeds, or other small objects to add to maps
- Glue
- String
- Cardboard

Standards Met in This Section

Common Core State Standards—Measurement and Data

Represent and interpret data.

Recognize perimeter as an attribute of plane figures and distinguish between linear and area measures.

Recognize area as an attribute of plane figures and understand concepts of area measurement (3.MD, National Governors Association Center for Best Practices and Council of Chief State School Officers [NGA Center and CCSSO] 2010, pp. 22, 25).

Introduce

Ancient mariners in the South Pacific were noted for their vast knowledge of sailing and navigation. These sailors were experts on wind and ocean currents, the locations of reefs, the types of seabirds and where they nested and flew, and the location and movement of stars throughout the year. Such mariners were highly respected in their communities and often taught apprentices their navigational knowledge, using "stick charts" or bamboo maps to depict vast areas of ocean and locations of islands. The charts themselves were typically not carried by the mariners while sailing but instead were maps to study while on dry land.

Stick charts were constructed using thin bamboo sticks that were tied together to create a grid-like pattern. Objects as shells, seeds, or bird feathers were attached across the grid to represent specific geographical locations that a navigator could use as location reference points. In addition to using the map to display an area of ocean, segments of the map and where objects were located on it helped navigators show distances and therefore calculate travel times on ocean voyages.

In this activity students will learn the concepts of perimeter and area as it relates to constructing representative maps of places where they live, play, and learn.

Explore and Create

1. Begin the activity by asking students to draw an example of a map of their community. Provide general guidance, but if asked encourage the students to draw as big or as small an area of their community as they wish. As children draw, ask them what particular features they are representing. Guide them to discovering how mapmakers typically use prominent objects that are easily recognizable to many to construct their maps. As novice mapmakers, they are doing the same.

2. Search the Internet for the term "stick charts," and share what you find with your students. Explain that these "charts" were maps used by ancient South Pacific mariners to navigate over thousands of miles.

3. Refer to a Pacific Region stick chart photo image you have accessed on the Internet and ask students to create a story of the oceans and islands represented. Ask them to discuss locations near and far from each other.

4. Explain the terms *area* and *perimeter,* and relate this explanation to the stick chart. What dimensions do they suggest for the length and width of the stick chart? Using the linear dimension of a single square in the grid, how many total squares are there in the map? Can the students determine a way to calculate area using the stick chart model?

Apply and Extend

- Solicit from the students some ideas of other things they could map, such as the classroom, school, playground, local community, or part of their community. List the ideas on the board and create student teams from those wishing to work on a particular idea. Have the teams draw maps representing these ideas.

- Discuss the area the students are trying to represent and the scale that they therefore will wish to use to construct their stick chart map. Students will soon discover the relationship between small-scale and complex charts or large-scale and more open charts. Students should select the scale that helps them to best achieve their goals.

- Provide the students with items in the Materials list above, and challenge them to create a physical stick chart map. Where sticks intersect, students can place a drop of glue and tie the sticks together with string or thread. After the glue dries, their map will be rigid. Students can collect or even make small objects to attach to their maps to represent special and important physical features.

- Challenge the students to display their finished maps on cardboard or poster board and to write a short description of their map and the place it represents. Make sure all students include a description of the perimeter and area of the space the map represents.

Summarize and Assess

Discussion Questions

Q Ancient navigators were very respected in their communities for the knowledge they possessed. Which professions can you name and describe where knowing mathematics and applying its concepts and principles are important in our society?

Q Most of us have used (or seen someone use) paper maps, or GPS as a navigational aid in an automobile. What skills must a mapmaker possess? What role does mathematics play in the designing of maps, whether ancient or modern?

Grades 4–8

Objectives

Students will create designs representing various models of Hawaiian weaving examples. They will note the transformations and iterations in various patterns, and they will analyze and name the shapes and angles found within the structure of the items.

Materials

- Grid paper
- Examples of Hawaiian or other Pacific Island weavings
- Paper
- Pencil
- Ruler
- Compass

Standards Met in This Section

Common Core State Standards—Geometry

Represent three-dimensional figures using nets made up of rectangles and triangles, and use these nets to find the surface area of these figures. Apply these techniques in the context of solving real-world and mathematical problems (6.G.4, NGA Center and CCSSO 2010, p. 45).

NCTM Standards—Geometry

- ▲ understand relationships among the angles, side lengths, perimeters, areas, and volumes of similar objects;
- ▲ explore congruence and similarity;
- ▲ describe sizes, positions, and orientations of shapes under informal transformations such as flips, turns, slides, and scaling; and
- ▲ examine the congruence, similarity, and line or rotational symmetry of objects using transformations (NCTM 2000, pp. 164, 232).

NCTM Standards—Measurement

- ▲ understand, select, and use units of appropriate size and type to measure angles, perimeter, area, surface area, and volume;
- ▲ select and apply techniques and tools to accurately find length, area, volume, and angle measures to appropriate levels of precision; and
- ▲ solve problems involving scale factors, using ratio and proportion (NCTM 2000, p. 240).

Introduce

The art of weaving coconut fronds into useful everyday household items is an ancient practice found in all tropical regions. People have always seemed to have a need to enhance everyday objects with beauty. Even though the decorative aspect does not make objects more useful, it does fulfill a basic human need for individual creativity.

Shapes are woven as patterns that decorate the Hawaii frond art. Similar shapes move in a pattern across the geometric plane of the decorated item. As these figures are moved about the plane, a limited number of motions are possible due to the physical limitations. There are exactly four types of these rigid motions possible in the limited space, or strip design patterns: (*a*) a *translation,* or slide, moving the figure forward repeatedly; (*b*) a *reflection,* or mirror image in a vertical, horizontal, or combination line; (*c*) a *rotation,* or movement around a fixed center point through 180 degrees; and (*d*) a *glide reflection,* a movement that first translates the figure and then reflects it.

The palm frond bracelets made by the lauhala weavers (as in fig. 8.2) incorporate a variety of patterns. These patterns are individual to each weaver and are often handed down from generation to generation. Since the bracelets are made with rectangular strips of the seasoned palm fronds, all the patterns exhibit geometric designs using squares, rectangles, parallelograms, and triangles. Every bracelet pattern can be made using one of the four types of rigid motion described above, or a combination of several motions.

Fig. 8.2. Lauhala bracelets made by Hawaiian crafter Teri Manawale'a Corpuz

Explore and Create

1. Provide examples of lauhala bracelets for your students such as those pictured above.

2. Discuss with your students the types of geometry figures that can be made with rectangular strips of palm fronds. What types of figures do they observe in the bracelets? How many different types of polygons are found in the designs? Identify the types of triangles found in the bracelets.

3. Which types of geometry figures, or polygons, are most often used in the bracelet designs? Are the polygons regular or irregular? Ask students to create a chart for recording the frequency with which they observe the different geometric shapes (see table 8.1).

Table 8.1
Polygon frequency chart

	Triangle	Square	Rhombus	Parallelo-gram	Rectangle
Bracelet 1					
Bracelet 2					
Bracelet 3					
Bracelet 4					

4. The different types of isometries that result from the movement of the figures in the plane are called *symmetry groups*. For any strip pattern, its symmetries can be classified as one being in one of seven distinctive groups:

— Translation

— Horizontal reflection

— Glide reflect

— Vertical reflection

— Rotation of 180 degrees

— Horizontal and vertical reflection

— Rotation/vertical reflection

5. Students should use examples of bracelet designs such as those above and examine them for the type of isometry shown in the weaving. They should have at least one example of each type of isometry to identify before they begin to create their own designs.

6. Provide students with grid paper to design their own bracelet patterns. They should make designs that use the isometries studied earlier with combinations of the basic geometry figures from the chart above.

7. Give each student an opportunity to show the bracelet design and to explain the figures and the isometries within the design.

Apply and Extend

- To make a bracelet to fit a particular individual, students need to think about the design in terms of standard measurements. Have students consider what they would need to do to make a bracelet to fit. For example, they would need to measure the wearer's wrist and then decide how much more to add for ease of fit. To make the bracelet have overall symmetry, a midpoint of the measurement should be taken. The use of the grid paper and rulers should be used in designing an exact-sized bracelet to be made.

Summarize and Assess

Discussion Questions

Q Which of the seven isometries did you find most difficult to use in designing a pattern for your bracelet?

Q After studying the patterns in the bracelets, where have you observed similar patterns around you in everyday life? Which of the isometries did you observe most often?

Q If you have done any of the activities in chapter 4, compare the designs and the weaving patterns of the lauhala bracelets with the beadwork designs from Native Americans. Discuss the similarities between the two and why they might have such similarities.

Grades 9–12

Objectives

Students will recreate models of South Pacific weaving samples and describe algorithmically the pattern iterations of each weaving strip along the item. They will then explore items that could be created using their understanding of the lauhala/coconut frond weaving criteria. Students will explore how pricing is set for such items once time, materials, shape, and size are considered.

Materials

- Paper
- Pencil
- Grid paper
- Ruler
- Protractor
- Compass
- Calculator
- Computer application

Standards Met in This Section
Common Core State Standards—Geometry
Apply geometric methods to solve design problems (e.g., designing an object or structure to satisfy physical constraints or minimize cost; working with typographic grid systems based on ratios) (G-MG.3, NGA Center and CCSSO 2010, p. 78).
NCTM Standards—Geometry
▲ analyze properties and determine attributes of two- and three-dimensional objects;   ▲ use Cartesian coordinates to analyze geometrical situations;   ▲ understand and represent translations, reflections, rotations, and dilations of objects in the plane by using sketches, coordinates, vectors, function notation, and matrices; and   ▲ use various representations to help understand the effects of simple transformations and their compositions (NCTM 2000, p. 308).
NCTM Standards—Measurement
▲ make decisions about units and scales that are appropriate for problem situations involving measurement (NCTM 2000, p. 320).
NCTM Standards—Algebra
▲ use symbolic algebra to represent and explain mathematical relationships; and   ▲ generalize patterns using explicitly defined and recursively defined functions (NCTM 2000, p. 296).

Introduce

To weave anything from a small bracelet to an elaborate and ornate container in the manner of South Pacific islanders, the weaving material must first be prepared. To use lauhala (the leaves of the hala tree), the leaves must be cut from the tree, dethorned, flattened, and dried for use. Long leaves—those that measure 8 feet or more in length—are preferred, because a minimum of splicing will be required for the weaving project.

The prepared lauhala are packaged and stored in circular rolls that contain from fifty to one hundred leaves. These rolls, called *kuka'a,* are easy to carry and stack for future projects or for sale. To make the kuka'a, the weaver begins with a long, sturdy hala leaf and secures its end to make a circle. To complete the kuka'a, the weaver then rolls leaves inside the circle. The process is continued until no more leaves can be inserted into the circle.

Leaves are typically about 4 inches in width, but they must be cut, or stripped, through various methods to the correct width for each project. Ancient Polynesians used long fingernails, bamboo spears, bones, shells, large thorns, and other sharp objects to cut the leaves to the desired width. Expert weavers can strip the leaves to the correct widths with a single steel pin.

Explore and Create

1. Many items—headbands, fans, bracelets, and some containers, for example—use strips from $1/8$ to $3/4$ inch wide for the weaving. Calculating the size of the kuka'a and the number of leaves used to make it can help students practice estimation and measurement skills. Discuss the relationships between circles and linear measurements such as the radius and diameter. Ratio and proportion skills can be reviewed as students use the indicated number of approximate leaves for the given width to find the number of leaves for the remaining kuka'as. Ask students to complete a chart similar to table 8.2.

Table 8.2
Leaf estimation chart

Width of *kuka'a*	Diameter	Radius	Area	Approximate number of leaves
18 inches				100
16 inches				
12 inches				
10 inches				

2. Discuss the process of stripping the leaves with students, and ask them to calculate the number of strips that can be made from different leaf widths. Have them investigate the varying widths of strips—such as $1/8$, $1/4$, $3/8$, $1/2$, $5/8$, $3/4$, and $7/8$ inches—that can be made from leaves varying in width from one to four inches. The investigation can extend to expressing the number of strips that can be made with an algebraic function.

3. Each of the bracelet strip patterns can be analyzed as one of the seven possible isometries identified above. To mathematically code the distinctive symmetry group, a system for classification has been developed by crystallographers, who first used the system to identify and code the patterns found in three-dimensional crystals. Each strip pattern can be identified as belonging to a particular symmetry group through a series of four characters:

- Character One, translation: If the pattern contains a translation, code it as a *p*.

- Character Two, vertical reflection symmetry: *m*, if has a line of vertical symmetry, or *1* if it does not.

- Character Three, horizontal/glide symmetry (such as your footprints would make in the sand): *m*, if it has a horizontal line of symmetry, *a*, if it has a glide reflection but not a horizontal line of symmetry, and *1*, if it has neither.

- Character Four, 180-degree rotation: *2*, if there is a point of 180-degree rotation, and *1*, if there is not.

This four-character classification system gives complete information about the symmetry groups of any strip patterns such as the lauhala bracelets. A bracelet coded as *pmm2* would indicate that it has a translation *(p)*, both vertical and horizontal symmetry *(m and m)*, and also a 180-degree rotation *(2)*.

4. Provide various examples from the Internet of lauhala bracelets for students to practice the mathematical coding, or (if they have access to computers) have students find their own examples. Students can record their mathematical codings on grid paper with a sketch of the bracelet design. They should be encouraged to compare their findings and discuss which of the isometries occurred most often, and which occurred least. What kind of geometric figures occur in the most symmetrical of the isometries?

Apply and Extend

- Students can extend their knowledge of the mathematical coding process by designing a bracelet design for each of the seven isometries. Depending on their access to technology, students can use grid paper or a computer application to create their designs.

- Students can further extend the exploration as they measure the angles involved in the designs. Discuss the types of angles they might expect to find in the geometry figures used and why these angles would be repeated in the weavings.

- Pattern comparisons of bracelets using the geometric coding of Internet images can made from different geographic regions of the South Pacific. Have students create a chart of locations/cultures and the most typical isometry used. After students analyze their data, can students infer that certain communities have a preference for a particular pattern (isometry), which differs in another?

Summarize and Assess

Discussion Questions

Q Other examples of strip patterns—and opportunities for the mathematical coding of the isometries of the patterns—can be found in Maori rafter patterns, Incan pottery, and Native American beadwork. Students can investigate one of these cultures or others for examples of the patterns. What differences and similarities can be seen?

Q Where might you find strip patterns similar to these in their everyday life? Why are these strip patterns so popular in all cultures?

Featured Consultant for This Chapter

Barbara Dougherty *holds the Richard G. Miller Endowed Chair of Mathematics Education at the University of Missouri. She has conducted classroom and student-based curriculum research and development for more than twenty years. Dougherty is recognized nationally and internationally for her work emphasizing teacher content knowledge and the implementation of effective, research-based instructional strategies.*

9

INDIA
Rangolee and Kolam Folk Art Designs

Locations The states of Maharashtra and Tamil Nadu, India

66 *Most children are visual learners. Rangolee is a very colorful, attractive, and easily reproducible mathematical art. Both children and adults get excited about the making and decorating of designs. Using this leverage, they are guided toward complex mathematical concepts and facts. Rangolee designs based on rectangular and hexagonal dot matrices provide an opportunity for teachers and students to learn and practice mathematics concepts.* 99

—*Madhuri Bapat*

Context

Rangolee and kolam are types of folk art that originated in several states and provinces in southern India; they are still practiced as a daily activity by women there. Rangolee designs, typically composed of geometric shapes, are decorative art drawn on the floors of living rooms and courtyards during Hindu festivals. The designs are meant to be sacred and welcoming to the visiting Hindu deities. Kolam designs have a similar appearance, though they are created with lines drawn around or through dot matrices using rice powder chalk. In Tamil Nadu (a state in southern India), women from all socioeconomic strata of life create a new kolam on the walkway to their homes daily. The designs welcome those who enter the home, and the rice powder can be considered a gift of food to the insects and birds that may consume it. The closed loops that are used to create the kolam deter evil or unwanted spirits from entering.

Fig. 9.1. Handmade Kolam design

Rangolee art has different names in the various provinces of India. The designs are inspired by ancient symbols passed down through the ages from generation to generation. The designs are typically created with locally available materials, such as colored sands, colored rice, dry flour, or flower petals. Rangolee designs are beautifully decorative, but they also are intended to bring good luck and replace any negative energy with a positive one. Women typically do rangolee during special occasions and festivals, weddings, and similar observances. Major symbols used in them include lotus flowers, mangoes, fish, birds, human figures, and geometry figures. The rangolee designs vary from simple geometric shapes to very elaborate designs made by numerous people. Some of these designs also have cultural significance and stories attached to them.

Kolam figures are designed by first creating a dot matrix. The number of dots used influences the size and types of designs as well as their complexity. The artisan draws the lines around the dots to create a continuous flow, trying to not draw over any line already constructed. This technique is said to illustrate how one must become aligned with the harmony found in life and nature. Interestingly, researchers and developers in the computer technology industry are studying these ancient designs today as new types of electronic circuits are developed.

Both of these types of designs are easy to create and fun to reproduce. One doesn't need to be an expert artist to draw and decorate them. Rangolee and kolam designs use both parts of the brain, as both logical and artistic capacities are engaged. The colorful designs attract children and engage them in learning, while deepening their understanding of mathematical concepts through this transfer of kinesthetic intelligence. Designs are often based on isometric, radial, and rectangular dot matrices similar to those contained within the NCTM standards. This ancient folk art from India makes an excellent interdisciplinary educational tool for all levels of students.

Kindergarten–Grade 3

Objectives

Students will create models of polygons (squares and triangles) when provided perimeter and area measures as they use those shapes to create rangolee designs.

Materials

- Colored paper
- Scissors
- Centimeter rulers
- Glue sticks

Standards Met in This Section

Common Core State Standards—Measurement and Data

Recognize perimeter as an attribute of plane figures and distinguish between linear and area measures.

Solve real world and mathematical problems involving perimeters of polygons, including finding the perimeter given the side lengths, finding an unknown side length, and exhibiting rectangles with the same perimeter and different areas or with the same area and different perimeters (3.MD.8, National Governors Association Center for Best Practices and Council of Chief State School Officers [NGA Center and CCSSO] 2010, p. 25).

NCTM Standards—Geometry

- recognize, name, build, draw, compare, and sort two- and three-dimensional shapes (NCTM 2000, p. 96).

NCTM Standards—Measurement

- explore what happens to measurements of a two-dimensional shape such as its perimeter and area when the shape is changed in some way (NCTM 2000, p. 170).

Introduce

A rangolee or kolam design is a colorful drawn image placed near a house entrance to welcome guests in India. These patterns are typically drawn with fingers dipped in locally available materials such as rice grains, flour, colored powder, chalk, and other painting materials.

Rangolee designs can be drawn in a variety of geometric shapes, such as squares, rectangles, circles, or a combination of all three. The patterns are composed of combinations of geometric shapes or illustrate animals and objects found in nature. Natural designs may include depictions of peacocks, swans, flowers, mangoes, leaves, and other natural elements. The designs display various types of lateral and rotational symmetry that communicate a sense of balance and order.

The designs were originally drawn in small patterns no larger than two feet square, but entire areas of the floor may now be covered with these intricate designs. To introduce students to this art, you can find pictures of rangolee patterns on the Internet, along with descriptions of the people who make and use them.

Explore and Create

1. After the students have been introduced to rangolee art, remark on how it reflects the way art and mathematics are combined to make beautiful and culturally important designs in parts of India. Show the students one selected picture of rangolee art. Have the class share insights as they describe the mathematical attributes they see in the design. For instance, students may note the types and number of shapes in the art. They may describe pattern or movement or perhaps talk about how one side is mirrored or reflected in the opposite side. The teacher should note these insights on the board or on a chart as students identify and discover some common characteristics of rangolee art. Ensure that correct labels are used to define specific shapes (e.g., equilateral triangle, isosceles triangle, right triangle, scalene triangle, and so on).

2. Students should select a shape they find pleasing in the art and draw that shape on paper. One student, for example, may like the look and shape of an equilateral triangle and draw it. Discuss with students the terms *perimeter* and *area*. Encourage students to draw their shape so that the perimeter does not exceed 20 centimeters. Note that some students approach this task by drawing and trying various side lengths until they create a shape that meets their standards. Other students may approach the task less visually and more mathematically. Discuss the shapes that are created and how they were designed, and have the students cut the shapes from their colored paper.

3. Students should use their first shape as a pattern to cut other similar shapes until they have enough shapes to begin designing a pattern (see fig. 9.2, for example). If children are allowed to explore, this creative act will be like second nature for most students.

4. As they create their own works of art, refer students back to the list or chart of rangolee design characteristics created above. Allow and encourage student communication and verbal interaction during this activity. When students have completed their projects, ask for volunteers to share their designs and share the "meaning" they wished to convey in their design. Teachers should make the most of every opportunity to emphasize vocabulary that highlights shape names, their attributes, and the symmetry of the unique class designs.

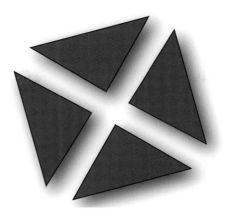

Fig. 9.2. Rangolee pattern with four triangles

Apply and Extend

- Continue using rangolee art as the context for examining of mathematical concepts and vocabulary by focusing specifically on the various types of triangles we study in math. First, on the board or on a chart write the following names of triangles:

  equilateral, isosceles, right triangle, and scalene

- Note that because all shapes are triangular that they have three sides. Next, draw a picture next to its label and ask students to help you define them. Particularly note terms such as angles (wide or narrow) and sides (long or short). Complete the chart that can be displayed in a prominent part of the classroom for all to see.

- Have students create a T-chart as shown in figure 9.3:

Triangle type	Perimeter	Length of each side

Fig. 9.3. Triangle T-chart

- Challenge the students to now work in pairs to create paper models of each triangle type with the same perimeter. Provide different colors and shades of paper. For instance, ask students to create triangle models where all perimeters are 40 centimeters. Observe the interactions taking place and the discussions ensuing.

- When students have completed their models, ask them to consider what triangle possesses the greatest area. Some students might think the areas will all be the same because the perimeters are. Ask if any students think so, and challenge them to determine if it is true. As this activity encourages critical thinking, resist the urge to tell students how to compute each area. Instead, encourage open discussion of how the different areas could be calculated. One group may decide to cut up their triangle and rearrange its parts into more of a quadrilateral. The quadrilaterals then could be placed on each other and areas compared. What do other groups suggest? Share and discuss ideas. The important part here is not that students immediately learn "the" formula for finding triangular areas, but rather that they consider the relationship between perimeter, area, and shape.

- Combine several pairs of students into larger teams. Invite these teams to create and paste their color triangular pattern pieces onto chart paper into rangolee designs. Encourage students to write a short comment on their chart describing a key insight they gained as a result of this activity.

Summarize and Assess

Discussion Questions

Q Do the designs studied in rangolee art remind you of designs created by any other cultures you have studied or experienced? If so, how? What might this say about how diverse people use mathematics to design art?

Q If art is used in mathematics, and mathematics is used in art, which one is more important and should come first? Why?

Grades 4–8

Objectives

Students will explore the numeric properties of various rangolee/kolam designs based on dot matrices. Students will explore dot patterns and calculate dot frequency as this relates to array models of multiplication.

Materials

- Construction paper
- Pencil

- Isometric dot paper (both rectangular and hexagonal; can be created online)
- Colored pencils

Standards Met in This Section
Common Core State Standards—Operations and Algebraic Thinking
Gain familiarity with factors and multiples. Generate and analyze patterns (4.OA, NGA Center and CCSSO 2010, p. 29).
NCTM Standards—Algebra
▲ describe, extend, and make generalizations about geometric and numeric patterns; and ▲ represent, analyze, and generalize a variety of patterns with words, graphs, and when possible, symbolic rules (NCTM 2000, pp. 158).

Introduce

The kolam figures made daily by the women of the Indian state of Tamil Nadu are traditionally created by drawing continuous lines around a series of dots on the ground. The figures resemble nets or even filigree designs. Often a dot design serves as the starting point when a figure is designed. Lines can then be drawn around or through the dots to connect them. In this activity, students will explore the interaction between the number of dots, their placement on a surface, and the resulting continuous line that is possible for making a figure.

Figure 9.4 shows some typical examples of both rangolee designs where dots are connected to form the patterns, and kolam designs where the design is made by drawing lines around the dots.

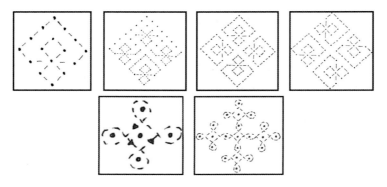

Fig. 9.4. Four rangolee designs (with lines connecting dots) and two kolam designs
(with lines around the dots)

Students can extend their understanding of basic geometry principles through the examination of these designs. As they examine the patterns provided to them, they can use appropriate geometry language and vocabulary to describe the symmetry and movements in the plane. Students can begin to explore algebraic relationships through the use of charts and graphs that describe the numbers of dots found within the iterations of the patterns. As students learn to understand the relationships of the geometric and algebraic principles found within the designs, they will be able to use this knowledge to make their own rangolee or kolam creations and further describe them in mathematical terms.

Explore and Create

1. Provide students with examples of rangolee or kolam such as those provided in the K–3 section. Ask students to provide an analysis of the design, including reflectional or rotational symmetry, similarity, and congruence of shapes within the design.

2. Have the students use grid paper to make a simple design using a square as the basic geometry structure. A convenient grid for beginners is a 15 × 15-centimeter grid with 3-centimeter intervals for the dots. Once the design is completed, they can identify the symmetry elements within it and find the perimeter and area of the design.

3. Ask students to make each type of design, both connecting the dots and drawing around the dots. What differences do they find in the two types of geometry structures produced by the two methods?

4. Using the information gained in the introduction of the activity, have students select one of the rangolee designs to transfer to the coordinate axes. Using their knowledge of reflectional symmetry, have students center the design on the origin (0, 0) and complete the drawing on the grid.

5. Have students extend their knowledge of coordinate geometry by labeling each of the design points with (x, y) notation.

6. Students can continue the exploration with one of the kolam designs and transfer it to the coordinate axes with the points labeled with (x, y) notation.

Apply and Extend

- Using the design on the coordinate axes, students can now begin to translate the design across the plane. They can begin by using a simple translation, a movement in the plane that repeats the pattern either vertically or horizontally.

- After they have translated the design, students can again label the new points with (x, y) notation. They can compare the corresponding points through the use of a table of values. Using the table of values, they should then be able to express the movement in the plane through an algebraic statement.

- Students can continue to change their designs through the use of motion movements in the plane and can use flips, slides, reflections, and rotations to make a more complex design.

Summarize and Assess

Discussion Questions

Q Compare the similarity and congruence elements of your design with another student's design. How are they alike? How do they differ?

Q Which geometry shapes are most difficult to translate? Why?

Q Compare the designs and their elements to those of the sona sand drawings of the Tshokwe people of northern Angola, southern Zaire, and western Zambia. Can you detect pattern similarities or differences in the designs and drawings? Discuss reasons that might explain these, focusing on the effects or geography and culture.

Grades 9–12

Objectives

Students will draw a line graph (straight line of the logarithmic graph) and make a prediction about how many dots there would be in additional iterations starting with a given figure. They will then write an equation for the line and write an expression to determine the number of dots needed to make higher iterations of a starting figure.

Materials

- Straightedge
- Pencil
- Isometric dot paper (both rectangular and hexagonal; can be created online)
- Colored pencils

Standards Met in This Section
Common Core State Standards—Operations and Algebra
Create equations that describe numbers or relationships (A-CED, NGA Center and CCSSO 2010, p. 65)
NCTM Standards—Algebra
▲ generalize patterns using explicitly defined and recursively defined functions; and   ▲ use symbolic algebra to represent and explain mathematical relationships (NCTM 2000, p. 296).

Standards Met in This Section *(continued)*

NCTM Standards—Geometry

- explore relationships (including congruence and similarity) among classes of two- and three-dimensional geometric objects, make and test conjectures about them, and solve problems involving them (NCTM 2000, p. 308).

Introduce

Kolam figures are created using dot matrices on or around which a line is drawn. Computer circuit designers study such traditional designs and figures to better understand the computer networks that are created; they use the insights gained to develop more efficient and powerful computing components. This reliance on the study of past cultural practices is yet another example of how computer scientists today are benefitting from the knowledge, skills, and intelligence of those who apply mathematics in the ways they live.

Explore and Create

1. Algebra can be used to examine the numbers of dots needed to increase the designs. Ask students to construct the image below (fig. 9.5) on their own paper.

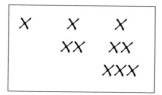

Fig. 9.5. Increasing numbers of dots in designs

2. Have students create a T-chart as shown in figure 9.6 and insert the data to represent the number of dots in each row and the total dots in each shape:

Number of Rows	Number of Dots in Row	Number of Dots in Total
1	1	1
2	3	4
3	6	10

Fig. 9.6. T-chart for increasing dots

3. What patterns do the students notice through analysis of this data? How many dots will there be in the fourth row, and how many total dots will there then be?

4. Challenge the students to verbally explain the pattern mathematically. Can they now create an algorithm used to communicate the explanation they have provided?

5. Challenge the students to explore constructing their own alternative dot matrices. Ask them to chart their tabulations and to develop both verbal and mathematical algorithmic expressions for their dot patterns. After students construct their dot matrix, encourage them to construct a kolam design that can result from their work.

Apply and Extend

- Ask students to use grid paper to create a square as depicted below:

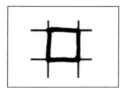

Fig. 9.7. Single grid square

- Point out that the square was constructed using four points or intersections of the grid paper lines. Ask students to again construct a graph describing the number of dots required to construct an iterative square design.

- Ask students to draw an iterative square pattern and complete the graph based on their activity.

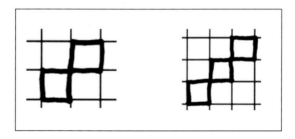

Fig. 9.8. Double and triple squares

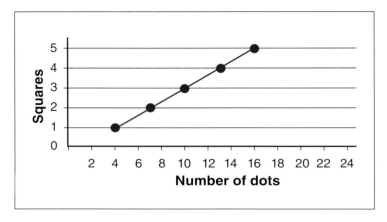

Fig. 9.9. Dots and squares chart

- What do the students predict will happen at the fourth and fifth iterative? What numeric pattern is emerging? Can they write an algorithm to describe the line that emerges when the total dot data is connected? Can they compose an algorithm to calculate the total number of dots necessary to complete the nth square iteration?

- Encourage students to explore the kolam designs they can create using different shapes and types of iterations. As they chart or graph their data, what relationships become apparent between patterns, shapes, and iterations?

Summarize and Assess

Discussion Questions

Q Researcher and author Reuben Hersh writes, "There's only one mathematics, indivisible now and forever. Mathematics is a single inseparable whole." How would you respond to him after experiencing multiple mathematical principles set in this Indian design context?

Q Researcher and author Marsha Ascher holds a different view. She explains, "Most cultures do not set mathematics apart as a distinct, explicit category. But with or without that category, mathematical ideas, nonetheless, do exist." Are Hersh and Ascher agreeing or disagreeing? In your opinion, does mathematics shape culture and do cultures adapt and influence mathematics to serve their own needs?

Q Compare the similarity and congruence elements of your design with another student's design. How are they alike? How do they differ?

Q Which geometry shapes are most difficult to translate? Why?

Q Compare the designs and their elements to those of the sona sand drawings of the Tshokwe people of northern Angola, southern Zaire, and western Zambia. Do your designs exhibit similar network theory?

Featured Consultant for This Chapter

Madhuri Bapat *is a professor of physics at Eastern Arizona College in Thatcher, Arizona. A native of India, she holds degrees in both nuclear and plasma physics. Madhuri has published several articles and instructional children's books on rangolee designs, kolam art, and sona designs from Africa. She often conducts workshops for teachers and students in the art of rangolee design.*

10

BULGARIA
Embroidery Patterns

Location   Northern region of Bulgaria

❝ *Mathematics describes our world through discovery and representation of the harmony and pattern that surround us. Traditional art captures the human desire to recreate worldviews in tangible aesthetic forms. By exploring the mathematical ideas embedded in traditional Bulgarian embroidery, learners uncover the intrinsic connections of mathematics to one's heritage and culture uniqueness.* ❞

—*Vessela Ilieva*

Context

Bulgaria is a country in Eastern Europe that is home to about seven and a half million people. Its area of 110,910 square kilometers (roughly 42,000 square miles) makes it about the size of the state of Virginia. Located in the southeastern corner of the European continent, the country borders Turkey and Greece to the south, Macedonia and Serbia to the west, Romania to the north, and the Black Sea to the east. Bulgaria's capital, Sofia, is in the western region of the country.

Bulgaria was founded in 681, and its rich history is reflected in its centuries-long traditions, a variety of cultural artifacts, and a number of transformative events. The last few decades of its history have been marked by significant changes in moving from a totalitarian government to a democracy. This transformation has had an effect on every aspect of the social, political, and economic life in the country, as it becomes established as a democratic country and as a member of the European Union since 2007.

Traditionally, the Bulgarian educational system has placed a strong emphasis on the importance of studying mathematics. In recent years, new curriculum requirements have increased the rigor of the mathematics that is studied. One of the signs of this change is the involvement of younger, elementary-age students in accelerated, in-depth mathematics studies. Across the country, magnet schools of mathematics with specifically designed mathematics curricula have been admitting students after seventh grade when they satisfactorily pass a rigorous problem-solving mathematics exam. Some of these schools now admit children after the fourth grade, when they must also pass a rigorous mathematics exam for acceptance.

One of the recognized symbols of Bulgaria around the world is cloth embroidery in multiple forms and formats. Embroidery is a traditional Bulgarian craft that represents its people's connections with nature, society, and other people. It is found predominantly on clothing such as shirts and skirts, and on household items such as pillowcases, table covers and runners, napkins, and other accessories.

Embroidery has a presence in most Bulgarian homes as a link to the rich and colorful Bulgarian culture and history. Even in the most trying times of their past, Bulgarians were able to keep much of their cultural heritage intact. Some of this can be attributed to native arts, such as their unique embroidery designs. Painstakingly created by the hands of Bulgarian women, embroidery has reflected their creativity, imagination, and skill for centuries.

The embroidery itself carries the spirit of what is traditionally Bulgarian. The dominating color for the embroidery is red, the traditional Bulgarian representation for health. In northern Bulgaria, embroidery is often stitched on a white cotton material for clothing or on white or beige cloth for household items. The threads used are most often made of cotton, wool, or silk, and their dominant colors are red, black, and white. Blue, green, and yellow threads are often included to add to the beauty of the pieces.

The embroidery designs vary in shape, as each one represents items from nature or life that are grouped into formations and related to the traditions of a specific region. As cultures have influenced each other through population movement and various historic events, similar embroidery motifs may be found on items throughout Europe, and the mathematical connections based on them may be related to artifacts specific to different regions of the world. Including the traditions and features of embroidery in the curriculum can help in preserving these rich artifacts for generations and in building deeper understanding of the distinctive culture they express.

Bulgarian embroidery is fascinating with its variety, fine detail, and unique beauty, as well as with the special thread of mathematics ideas found within it. For example, Koch curves can be found in most richly embroidered Bulgarian folk costumes. The embroidery's patterns and shapes symbolize what is truly beautiful, original, and uniquely Bulgarian.

Kindergarten–Grade 3

Objectives

Students will explore various shapes, along with their terms and definitions. They will chart shape names and list their number of sides. Students will use observations and pattern analysis to explore and create shapes creating variations of embroidery templates. They will draw and cut paper to create models of traditional embroidery patterns. Extending their charting, they will count and record the number of sides of each pattern as more shapes and rotations are added.

Materials

- Pictures (or original pieces if available) of traditional Bulgarian embroidery (tablecloths, napkins, shirts, blouses, etc.)
- Card stock
- Pencil
- Colored pencils
- Scissors

Standards Met in This Section

Common Core State Standards—Geometry

Understand that shapes in different categories (e.g., rhombuses, rectangles, and others) may share attributes (e.g., having four sides), and that the shared attributes can define a larger category (e.g., quadrilaterals). Recognize rhombuses, rectangles, and squares as examples of quadrilaterals, and draw examples of quadrilaterals that do not belong to any of these subcategories (3.G.1, National Governors Association Center for Best Practices and Council of Chief State School Officers [NGA Center and CCSSO] 2010, p. 26).

NCTM Standards—Geometry

- analyze characteristics and properties of two- and three-dimensional geometric shapes and develop mathematical arguments about geometric relationships;
- specify locations and describe spatial relationships using coordinate geometry and other representational systems;
- apply transformations and use symmetry to analyze mathematical situations; and
- use visualization, spatial reasoning, and geometric modeling to solve problems (NCTM 2000, p. 164).

Introduce

People throughout the world use patterns incorporating shape and color not only in creating works of art, but they often integrate pattern, color, and shape to decorate and beautify items of daily use. These items may include clothing, household items, or religious objects. Particular patterns created by specific communities can be used to identify where the people using those objects live and what cultural traditions they practice. Bulgarian embroidery illustrates this through its application of geometric patterns influenced by culture. Patterns are often used to convey certain significance or to honor what is valued. In Bulgarian embroidery, plants, animals, and other elements of nature are symbolically depicted in the various patterns the craft workers produce.

Explore and Create

1. Show students a world map and locate the country of Bulgaria. Share some basic important facts about the country such as its population, its relative size to other places the students may be aware of, and some of the educational standards and issues found in Bulgaria. Teachers should discuss how, as with many other countries in the world, the demographics of Bulgaria are changing as more immigrants are moving there to seek work and a better life. The Bulgarian educational system is working to ensure that all children in their schools receive a good education with a particular focus on helping students to develop optimal math skills.

2. Show students several examples of Bulgarian embroidery, and ask them to draw a picture to represent what they see. Figure 10.1 shows an example of an embroidery design. Students should then label the various shapes they identify within their designs. Provide the students with scissors, card stock, and glue sticks, and ask them to each create a model of their design. Lastly, students should count and complete the chart shown in figure 10.2 identifying the shapes, their number of sides, and their frequency in the design they have drawn.

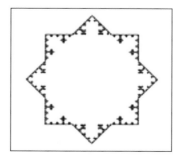

Fig. 10.1. Embroidery sample diagram

Shape	Sides	# of Shapes in Design

Fig. 10.2. Shapes and sides chart

Apply and Extend

- Once again, students are provided with scissors, card stock, and glue sticks, and they are asked to cut out a geometric shape of their choosing at least 10 centimeters wide and long. This initial shape becomes the main template for their design. Students may then explore shapes and patterns created from the various additional shapes they have cut and apply them to make their own designs. Students may wish to add color to their designs and should be encouraged to create a design that represents a topic or theme they value. When the designs are complete, students should once again add information to a chart (see fig. 10.2) about their design and consider how the shapes used, their frequency, and their positions affect the outcome of the design itself.

Summarize and Assess

Discussion Questions

Q When students come from different places and cultures, how can art be used to help teach both mathematics and the things they value in their culture?

Q As you created your own designs using concepts reflective of Bulgarian embroidery, what did you notice about how shapes and the number of them used related to how complex a design was?

Q Should the most complex shapes be considered to be the most beautiful or the most mathematical?

Grades 4–8

Objectives

Students will explore the use of ratios and proportional relationships through the use of geometry as they study Bulgarian embroidery and design their own patterns for it. They will describe the types of symmetry and ratios present in these patterns. Students will solve problems involving scale drawings of geometric figures, including computing actual lengths and areas from a scale drawing and reproducing a scale drawing at a different scale as they increase and decrease their patterns.

Materials

- Paper
- Pencil
- Graph paper
- Straightedge
- Compass
- Protractor
- Colored pencils

Standards Met in This Section

Common Core State Standards—Geometry

Understand that a two-dimensional figure is similar to another if the second can be obtained from the first by a sequence of rotations, reflections, translations, and dilations; given two similar two-dimensional figures, describe a sequence that exhibits the similarity between them (8.G.4, NGA Center and CCSSO 2010, p. 56).

NCTM Standards—Geometry

- explore congruence and similarity;
- investigate, describe, and reason about the results of subdividing, combining, and transforming shapes;
- make and use the coordinate systems to specify locations and to describe paths;
- examine the congruence, similarity, and line or rotational symmetry of objects using transformations; and
- recognize and apply geometric ideas and relationships in areas outside the mathematics classroom, such as art, science, and everyday life (NCTM 2000, pp. 164, 232).

Introduce

A common, unifying theme for all people, of all times and cultures, is the love of art and the use of it for beautifying everyday, utilitarian objects. The artwork does not make the object any more useful, but the need to impose an order and beauty on personal objects is found in all cultures. The Bulgarian designs on clothing and household objects such as tablecloths, napkins, and towels exhibit mathematically precise art worked in embroidery threads.

The embroidery patterns were developed during the years when Bulgaria was a part of the Turkish Empire. These patterns were unique and identified Bulgarian people as having a separate identity from the rest of the Turkish Empire. This embroidery was often done on clothing items and thus became integrated into regional costumes for both the men and women of Bulgaria.

Explore and Create

1. Have students review the basic concepts of symmetry and identify the types of symmetry found within Bulgarian patterns. Traditional Bulgarian patterns can be found in books or on websites. Provide students with embroidery patterns to use in identifying properties of symmetry.

Fig. 10.4. Embroidery pattern

2. Remind students of the meanings of *reflectional* and *rotational symmetry.*

3. Using one of the patterns provided, have students use a mirror to examine the design for reflectional symmetry. They can then begin to identify the axis of symmetry and study the effect of motions used in geometry. Are the axes always horizontal or vertical? Can a pattern have both vertical and horizontal axes of symmetry? Identify a pattern that has both.

4. Using another pattern, have students use their mirrors to find the rotational axes of symmetry. Students should find the center of the picture as they examine the design for a rotational symmetry. How many degrees are in a circle? How would you use a part of the circle to identify the angle of rotation? How many axes of symmetry do you think might be contained within a design?

5. Once students are comfortable with the concepts of reflectional and rotational symmetry, they are ready to create their own designs that exhibit these patterns of geometry motion. Using the grid paper, students should draw designs that show axis lines that are horizontal, vertical, both, or neither.

6. Using the grid paper, students should show their understanding of rotational symmetry by drawing designs that have angles of rotation of 180 degrees, 120 degrees, and 90 degrees.

7. Students can further explore the ideas of symmetry by examining the designs of other students in the class. How are their designs similar to each other? Do any of the designs have both reflectional and rotational symmetry? If color is added to the design, how does that change its rotational symmetry, or does it stay the same?

8. Using the grid paper, have students draw the following figures:

scalene triangle	square	trapezoid
isosceles triangle	rectangle	regular hexagon
equilateral triangle	rhombus	circle

Each figure can then be examined for reflectional and rotational symmetry. How many axes of symmetry does each one have? What is the angle of rotation for each of the figures?

Apply and Extend

- Provide students with a Bulgarian embroidery design and ask them to examine it for reflectional and rotational symmetry.

- Students should select one of the patterns they designed in an earlier assignment. They can now use the design to practice scale factors, ratios, and proportions.

- Using the grid paper to measure, have students record the pattern measurements.

- What do the measurements become when the pattern is doubled? Tripled? Halved?

- What if the pattern needs to be one and a half times as large? How would this problem be set up to find the correct measurements? What equation would be used?

- Using the grid paper as coordinate axes, find the significant coordinates of the design. Use ratios to find new coordinates for the design if it is halved, increased by one and a half, and doubled.

Summarize and Assess

Discussion Questions

Q   What properties do the geometric figures that have lines of symmetry have in common?

Q   What properties do the geometric figures that have rotational symmetry have in common?

Q   In reviewing Bulgarian embroidery designs, which type of symmetry is most often used? Why do you think this is the most common?

Q   To design a Bulgarian embroidery pattern, what geometry principles are used?

Q   How would you advise someone to begin designing one of these patterns?

Grades 9–12

Objectives

Students will review the properties of reflectional and rotational symmetry through the examination of Bulgarian embroidery designs. They will then extend their knowledge of symmetry principles and use it to describe and draw designs in the coordinate plane. Students will explore embroidery designs and calculate the increasing length of a pattern segment when considering the different orders of Koch curves present.

Materials

- Paper
- Grid paper
- Tracing paper
- Calculator
- Pencil

Standards Met in This Section

Common Core State Standards—Geometry

Given a geometric figure and a rotation, reflection, or translation, draw the transformed figure using, e.g., graph paper, tracing paper, or geometry software. Specify a sequence of transformations that will carry a given figure onto another (G-CO.5, NGA Center and CCSSO 2010, p. 56).

NCTM Standards—Geometry

- use Cartesian coordinates and other coordinate systems to analyze geometric situations;

- investigate conjectures and solve problems involving two- and three-dimensional objects represented with Cartesian coordinates;

- understand and represent translations, reflections, rotations, and dilations of objects in the plane by using sketches, coordinates, vectors, function notation, and matrices;

- use various representations to help understand the effects of simple transformations and their compositions; and

- use geometric ideas to solve problems in, and gain insights into, other disciplines and other areas of interest such as art and architecture (NCTM 2000, p. 308).

NCTM Standards—Measurement

- make decisions about units and scales that are appropriate for problem solving situations involving measurement (NCTM 2000, p. 320).

Introduce

Bulgarian embroidery designs are unique to the people of this region, and the embroidery used on clothing and household objects vary from simple designs to the very complex. Students will build on their previous knowledge of reflectional and rotational symmetry as they examine different embroidery designs. They should be familiar with the axes of symmetry for different geometric figures, and they can use this knowledge as they translate designs in the coordinate plane.

Students will combine their knowledge of algebra with geometry as they both draw and algebraically describe the motion of the design as it is translated on the coordinate plane. They can further extend their knowledge of geometry as they examine the complex designs for evidence of fractal patterns within them. Using the information about fractal patterns, they can begin to design their own fractals through the use of basic geometric figures.

Explore and Create

1. Provide examples of Bulgarian embroidery for students to examine and classify according to the types of symmetry found within each piece.

2. Review the differences between reflectional and rotational symmetry. Remind students about the differences in coordinates when reflecting across the *x*-axis and the *y*-axis.

3. Using the Bulgarian embroidery examples, have students use the tracing paper to reproduce one or more of the patterns on a coordinate grid. Students should center one of the designs on the origin and another one slightly off center.

4. Using the pattern on the grid paper, students should then find and label the major coordinates of the outline.

5. Using the pattern on the coordinate grid, ask students to sketch the reflection of the design over the line $y = x$.

6. Students can then find and label the coordinates of the vertices of the reflection.

7. Using the original pre-image and the reflected image, students should then determine the relationship between a point and its image over the line of reflection.

Apply and Extend

- Select an embroidery design that exhibits a fractal pattern. Students should then examine the design and identify the basic geometric shape of the pattern.

- Fractals such as the Cantor set or the Sierpinski triangle can be used as examples of a fractal formation.

- Using the notion of fractals, have students make a fractal design using grid paper. One of the most basic fractals can be formed using an equilateral triangle. Each side of the triangle is divided into thirds with three smaller triangles drawn in the middle third of each side of the triangle. Continue the same iteration on each of the new triangles.

Summarize and Assess

Discussion Questions

Q What geometry principles are evident in the Bulgarian embroidery designs?

Q Which geometry principles occur most often in the patterns?

Q Do the types of principles vary by regional areas of Bulgaria?

Featured Consultant for This Chapter

Vessela Ilieva *is currently an associate professor of education at Utah Valley University in Orem, Utah. She dedicates her teaching and research to mathematics and culturally relevant education.*

NORTHERN
UNITED STATES
Two-Sided Dice of the
Potawatomi

Locations   Potawatomi tribal areas in the upper Mississippi River
region of the United States

66 *It is important for American Indian students to see
the mathematics in the traditional activities of their
culture. The two-sided dice game has been played for
hundreds of years by most tribes in North America,
and students continue to enjoy the game and learn the
mathematics incorporated in it.* 99

—*Richard Sgarlotti*

Context

The Potawatomi are an American Indian people living in the upper regions of the
Mississippi River. As members of the Algonquin family, the Potowatomi historically
allied themselves with the Ojibwe and Ottawa Nations in an alliance known as the
Council of the Three Fires. The Potawatomi first lived in lower Michigan, then moved to
northern Wisconsin and eventually settled into northern Indiana and central Illinois.

During the late 1800s and early 1900s, the Potawatomi aligned with the Tecumseh
Confederacy and participated in wars being fought between the British and the Americans, striving to protect their lands, culture, and ways of life. In the early 19th century,
major portions of Potawatomi lands were seized by the U.S. government. Following the
Treaty of Chicago in 1833, most of the Potawatomi people were forcibly removed from
their original lands. Many perished en route to new lands in the west through Iowa,
Kansas, and Oklahoma following what became known as the "Trail of Death." Remaining Potawatomi purchased land in Illinois and Indiana. Today, the Nation is again

growing and comprises an estimated population of more than 28,000. Tribal gaming enterprises and other business efforts are generating revenues used to build a strong economic infrastructure for the Nation as health, education, and other services are being provided to the people.

Games of chance involving concepts of probability are found in cultures around the world. All Native tribes have been documented as having played games of chance using locally available materials. American Indian cultures often used "stick dice," peach pits, or crafted two-sided disks from locally gathered materials as objects for their games. The Potawatomi, like other Native groups across the continent, enjoyed game playing, especially those games that involved the element of chance and probability.

The games of chance played by Native tribes can be classified into two types: (1) games in which some type of dice are randomly thrown and the resulting sum is kept by means of sticks, pebbles, bones, scratch marks, etc.; and (2) games in which one or more players makes a guess to determine where an odd marker is hidden, with success or failure recorded as a gain or loss of counters such as bones, sticks, pebbles, etc.

The basic elements for all the games of the first type consist of the dice and the items used for keeping count during the game. Most tribes in North America used two-sided dice sometimes during healing ceremonies, and at other times for amusement. The dice used for the games generally have two faces, different in either color or markings. They are made of a wide variety of materials, whatever is readily available where the tribe is located. Materials include split canes, wooden pieces, beaver teeth, woodchuck teeth, walnut shells, peach or plum pits, grains of corn, antler buttons, or disks made of bone, shell, brass, or pottery.

The dice are either thrown by hand or tossed in a basket or bowl. The dice thrown by hand are tossed into the air to fall on the ground or else are thrown against a hide or blanket. The basket or bowl dice game is most commonly played by women. In one variation, four to ten dice were shaken in a moccasin, basket, or other container and then tossed onto a surface, with a winner determined by achieving an equal number up and down.

There are two general types of counting methods for the dice games: (1) scoring kept with counters, such as sticks, bones, stones, etc.; and (2) scoring kept with a counting board, with sticks or twigs grouped in multiples of ten, or rarely in multiples of twelve. The game ends when one of the opposing sides has won all the counters.

The Potawatomi game (Kwezage'win) was traditionally played only by women, and mostly in the winter in place of a lacrosse-like game named double-ball. (In our version of the game in this chapter, both boys and girls will have a chance to experience this aspect of Native culture.) As with similar dice games from other tribes, a woman who wishes to honor her guardian spirit sponsors the game and ensures that the appropriate ceremonies are conducted prior to playing it. A special feast is held and certain rituals are followed. The bowl and dice pictured in figure 11.1 are in the collection of the National Museum of the American Indian. An interactive image and version of the game can be found at http://www.potawatomilanguage.org/virtualmuseum/dicegame.php.

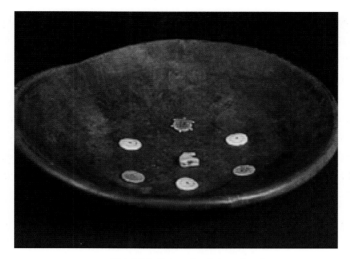

Fig. 11.1. Potawatomi game bowl

After the feast, a blanket is spread out on the floor and the women sit in a circle, but divided into two teams with each side sitting in a semi-circle facing the other. As many women can participate as want to play, but there are only four prizes: yard goods of red, blue, green, and white. The gaming equipment consists of a flat wooden bowl approximately eleven inches in diameter, and eight dice, six of which are thin, circular discs. One disk is carved in the form of a turtle and another as a horse's head. Dice were formerly made of buffalo rib, but horse's ribs are used today. One surface of each die is colored blue (red may also be used). Thus each die has a colored and a white side.

To play the game, one woman holds the bowl with both hands, and the dice are shaken to the far side of the bowl. The bowl is then given one flip, set on the floor, and the score counted, as follows:

All of similar color except 2	1 point
All of similar color except 1	3 points
All of similar color except turtle	5 points
All of similar color except horse	10 points
All of similar color	8 points
All of similar color except turtle and horse	10 points

The score is tallied by the woman laying out the correct number of bean or seed counters in front of her. Each woman shakes the bowl and collects points until she misses twice. A turn is considered a miss if none of the above combinations occur and no points are collected. She then passes the bowl to the next woman player in a clockwise rotation. The first to score ten points wins the game, and a piece of the yard goods is given to one of the men spectators, who then returns a gift of equal value for future games.

Kindergarten–Grade 3

Objectives

Students explore the basic concepts of probability by playing a variation of the Potawatomi game Kwezage'win. After observing the results, and then organizing and displaying their data, they will be able to make inferences based on these data. They will begin to understand basic probability ideas through their use in of game playing.

Materials

- Four two-sided dice per student
- Plastic mats on desks to use as "the blanket" for tossing the dice
- Paper plates to use as simulated baskets for tossing the dice
- Notebook paper
- Pencil
- A copy of a recording chart, one per student
- Large paper for recording class results

Standards Met in This Section
Common Core State Standards—Measurement and Data
Generate measurement data by measuring lengths of several objects to the nearest whole unit, or by making repeated measurements of the same object (2.MD.9, National Governors Association Center for Best Practices and Council of Chief State School Officers [NGA Center and CCSSO] 2010, p. 20.)
NCTM Standards—Data Analysis and Probability
▲ pose questions and gather data;
▲ represent data using concrete objects, pictures, and graphs; and
▲ describe parts of the data and the set of data as a whole to determine what the data show (NCTM 2000, p. 108).

Introduce

The Potawatomi are a part of the linguistic group known as the Central Algonquins. The Algonquin language was at one time the most widespread linguistic family in North America. Many of their words are now a part of America's vocabulary. *Hickory, hominy, moccasin, moose, wigwam,* and *woodchuck* are all Algonquin words. The traditional home-lands of the Algonquin were located in the northern woodlands, between the eastern and western borders of Lake Michigan and Lake Huron. These people were hunters, fisher-men, and farmers in the vast leafy forests of the eastern United States.

The harsh woods of the north often brought cold air and early winters. During the long winter months, the game of Kwezage'win was played by the Potawatomi. Students will be able to explore basic probability ideas through two versions of the game of Kwezage'win. They will begin to recognize patterns and repeated iterations as they use the two-sided dice and record their results.

Explore and Create

1. Discuss the meaning of informal probability with the students, using words they are familiar with, such as *probably, likely to happen,* or *might occur.* Continue the discussion to include what might happen when students play a simple variation of the Kwezage'win game using one two-sided die.

2. In this variation of the game, only one two-sided (plain and colored) die is tossed. Each student should toss the die ten times and record the results with a check mark in a chart similar to table 11.1. The results are also summarized into a total graph for the class.

Table 11.1
Results frequency chart with one two-sided die

Trial number	Red	No red
1		
2		
3		
4		
5		
6		
7		
8		
9		
10		
Totals		

3. Students should then observe the results and, as a class, find the ratio of plain to colored tosses as well as the fraction of plain and colored tosses. Students should also find the fractions of plain tosses to total tosses and colored tosses to total tosses. Students can compare their individual results with others' results and the class total. How are their results alike? How are they different? Why are the results different? Would they get the same totals if they tossed the die another ten times?

4. Remind students of their results in the previous version of the game. They can now extend their thinking about probability by using four dice. Discuss what the possible results might be for each toss. What results would they expect to see most often? What results would they expect to see the least?

5. In this variation of the game, students have four two-sided dice. The dice can be made from a variety of materials, or two-sided counters work well. Working in pairs, students should take turns shaking and tossing the dice ten times each. Shake and toss all four dice from the basket ten times, recording the results. Each pair of students can compare their likenesses and differences on the results of each toss. After students have compared their individual results, all results can be recorded on a class chart (such as table 11.2) for a comparison with a larger sample size. Make a check mark for the result on each toss.

Table 11.2
Frequency chart with four two-sided dice

Trial number	No red	1 red	2 red	3 red	4 red
1					
2					
3					
4					
5					
6					
7					
8					
9					
10					
Totals					

- How many tosses resulted in at least one pair of colored sides up?
- How many tosses resulted in no colored sides up?
- Which pattern resulted most often? Was it 0, 1, 2, 3, or 4 red sides up?

Apply and Extend

- Using the information from the table above, make a bar graph of the number of "red" dice results plotted for 0, 1, 2, 3, and 4 red sides on a toss.
- Compare your graph with your partner's results. How are they similar? How are they different?

- Why do you think the graphs are different?

- If you tossed the dice ten more times, how many times would you expect to get at least one pair of colored sides up?

- Try tossing the dice ten more times and record the results. Compare the similarities and differences with the first ten tosses.

- Which pattern will occur most often? Which one has the highest probability of occurring?

Summarize and Assess

Discussion Questions

Q The two preceding activities explored the probabilities of a tossed die resulting in a "red" or "not red." What fraction would you use to describe the probability of this occurrence?

Q What other examples can you give that model similar probabilities? Can you give fractional numbers to these probabilities?

Grades 4–8

Objectives

Students will explore basic properties of probability through playing a version of Kwezage'win, the Potawatomi two-sided dice game. They will begin to develop and evaluate predictions based on their observations of the data created through playing the game. They will then apply concepts of probability to new situations and extend their understanding of probability, including organizing, displaying, and analyzing data.

Standards Met in This Section

Common Core State Standards—Statistics and Probability

Understand that the probability of a chance event is a number between 0 and 1 that expresses the likelihood of the event occurring. Larger numbers indicate greater likelihood. A probability near 0 indicates an unlikely event, a probability around $1/2$ indicates an event that is neither unlikely nor likely, and a probability near 1 indicates a likely event.

Develop a probability model and use it to find probabilities of events. Compare probabilities from a model to observed frequencies; if the agreement is not good, explain possible sources of the discrepancy (7.SP.5 and 7, NGA Center and CCSSO 2010, pp. 50, 51).

Introduce

Students can further their understanding of basic probabilities by playing the game of Kwezage'win. They can use markers or paints to decorate each side of their dice. The traditional colors used are red and white, but students might be offered the opportunity to select colors of their own choice.

Explore and Create

1. Have the students divide into pairs. Each student in each pair will toss four two-sided dice at least five times and record the number of distinct pairs that occur. By working in pairs, students can compare individual results for similarities and differences. Students should make a check mark for the result on each toss in a chart such as table 11.3.

Table 11.3
Pairs frequency chart with four two-sided dice

Trial number	No pairs	1 red pair	2 red pairs	1 red/ 1 white	1 white pair
1					
2					
3					
4					
5					

2. Students should consider the following questions:

- Which outcome (number of pairs) occurred most often?
- Was this the same result as that of your working partner?
- Which outcome occurred least often? Why do you think this happened?

3. As each pair of students reports their outcomes, class results can be examined. Students should complete the chart in table 11.4 as indicated for each student in the class, while the class tally is recorded for all students to see. Extend the chart for as many students as needed.

Table 11.4
Class results of pairs frequency for tossing four two-sided dice

	Student name	# of tosses	# of red pairs	# of white pairs
1				
2				
3				
4				
5				
6				
7				
8				
9				
10				
11				
12				
13				
14				
15				
16				
17				
18				

4. Students should then use the information in the chart to make a bar graph depicting the total outcomes for the class.

5. Ask the students to describe how the graphs help to organize the information, and to suggest any other types of graphs that might be used for the information.

Apply and Extend

- Students can begin to formulate more complex ideas about probability through considering probability with independent events. Students should use one of the two-sided dice to experience the use of probabilities and create tree diagrams to establish independent-event probabilities. Student should first calculate individual probabilities, such as the probability of getting a red on one toss ($1/2$) or a white ($1/2$) and discuss what the numerators and denominators indicate.

- Have students toss a two-sided die and record the outcome, and then have them toss it again. Ask them what is the probability of getting a red on the first toss, and what is the probability of getting red a second time? Point out that these two tosses of the die are independent because they don't have any influence on each other. Whatever the first outcome is does not affect the next toss of the die.

- Make a tree diagram (such as fig. 11.2) to illustrate the outcomes for two tosses and to calculate the more complex probabilities of more tosses.

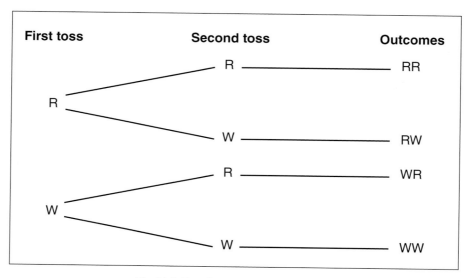

Fig. 11.2. Tree diagrams for toss outcomes

- There are four possible outcomes. Have students use the tree diagram to think about the results and answer the following questions:
  - How many ways can you get (RR)?
  - How many ways can you get (WW)?
  - How many ways can you get one red and one white? Order is not important.
  - What is the probability of RW (in either order)?

— What is the probability of two RR?

— What is the probability of two WW?

— What is the total for all the probable outcomes (RR, RW, WR, WW)?

Summarize and Assess

Discussion Questions

Q How will the probabilities change with the addition of four more dice in the game?

Q How would you explain the different points provided in the rules for scoring?

Q Why are some outcomes worth only one point while others are worth 10?

Grades 9–12

Objectives

Students will apply the general "multiplication rule" in a uniform probability model— $P(A \text{ and } B) = P(A)P(B|A) = P(B)P(A|B)$—as they explore basic properties of probability through simulated game play of the game Kwezage'win.

Materials

- Eight two-sided dice per person, or pair of students, with two of the dice to represent the horse and the turtle dice
- Plastic desk mats to use as the "blanket" for tossing the dice
- Paper plates to use as simulated baskets for tossing the dice
- Notebook paper
- Pencil
- Calculator
- Recording charts
- Large class chart for recording all results

Standards Met in This Section

Common Core State Standards—Statistics and Probability

Develop a probability distribution for a random variable defined for a sample space in which theoretical probabilities can be calculated; find the expected value (S-MD.3, NGA Center and CCSSO 2010, p. 83).

Standards Met in This Section *(continued)*
NCTM Standards—Data Analysis and Probability
▲ understand the concepts of sample space and probability distribution and construct sample spaces and distributions in simple cases;
▲ use simulations to construct empirical probability distributions;
▲ compute and interpret the expected value of random variables in simple cases;
▲ understand the concepts of conditional probability and independent events; and
▲ understand how to compute the probability of a compound event (NCTM 2000, p. 324).

Introduce

Randomization is an important concept in probability and data analysis. Randomization has two important uses in drawing accurate conclusions. First, collecting data from a random sample of a population makes it possible to then draw valid conclusions about the entire population. Second, in treatments such as medicine, randomly assigning individuals to different groups allows a fair comparison of the effectiveness of those treatments.

A statistically significant outcome is one that is not likely to happen as a result of chance alone, and this can be evaluated through the concept of randomization. Data collection and the conditions under which the data are collected are important when drawing accurate conclusions from the data.

Random processes can be described mathematically through the use of a probability model: the *sample space*, or possible outcomes, each of which is assigned a probability based on a random event. In situations such as tossing a two-sided die, rolling a number cube, or drawing a card, various outcomes seem equally likely. In a probability model, sample points represent outcomes and combine to make up events; probabilities of events can be computed by applying rules for independent and dependent events.

Review with your students the information and rules from earlier in the chapter for playing Kwezage'win, the two-sided dice game of the Potawatomi. They can use the game and the outcomes of the dice as a basis for further exploration of basic probability and rules for independent and dependent events.

Remind students of basic probabilities and how they are computed using a sample space and probable outcomes. With a two-sided die (one colored, one plain), the odds of one die coming up on the colored side is one out of two ($1/2$).

Explore and Create

1. Have students answer the questions and fill out a table (such as table 11.5) with the theoretical probabilities.

Table 11.5
Probabilities of colored dice being thrown

With one die, the probability of no colored die being rolled is $1/2$.
With two dice, the probability of no colored is _____
With three dice, the probability of one colored is _____
With four dice, the probability of two colored is _____
With five dice, the probability of three colored is _____
With six dice, the probability of four colored is _____
With seven dice, the probability of five colored is _____
With eight dice, the probability of six colored is _____

Note: The six situations above are the same as "All of similar color except 2," and count 1 point according to the rules of the game.

2. Working in pairs, each student should toss the dice ten times and record the number of colored dice for each event in a table such as table 11.6.

Table 11.6
Results for numbers of colored dice per roll

Trial	0	1	2	3	4	5	6	7	8
1									
2									
3									
4									
5									
6									
7									
8									
9									
10									

(Number of colored dice)

3. What do the experimental results show? Students should compare results in each pair. How are they the same? How are they different?

4. Combine the results from all students in class. Students should compare the total results with their own chart. Why are they different?

5. Ask students to find the experimental probabilities for each of these events using the table above.

> — All of similar color except 1—counts 3 points
>
> — All of similar color except turtle—counts 5 points
>
> — All of similar color except horse—counts 10 points
>
> — All of similar color—counts 8 points
>
> — All of similar color except turtle and horse—counts 10 points

Apply and Extend

- Ask students to find the theoretical probabilities for each of these events using probability rules.

> — All of similar color except 1—counts 3 points
>
> — All of similar color except turtle—counts 5 points
>
> — All of similar color except horse—counts 10 points
>
> — All of similar color—counts 8 points
>
> — All of similar color except turtle and horse—counts 10 points

- Ask students to answer the following questions: How do the experimental and theoretical probabilities differ? Why do you think they are different?

- Have the students consider what might happen if they tossed the dice ten more times. Would the results be the same or different?

- Students may design a scoring system based on the theoretical probabilities they found and explain the reasoning for their system.

Summarize and Assess

Discussion Questions

Q Archaeologists have found evidence of games of chance in prehistoric digs, showing that gaming and gambling have been major pastimes for different peoples since the dawn of civilization. How does this affect how you think of math and its early applications?

Q What other games that use the concept of randomization and chance have you played? What cultures invented these games? Some possible examples include Parcheesi (Indian) and Senet (Egyptian).

Q Considering the great mathematical discoveries of ancient civilizations such as Greek, Egyptian, Chinese, and Indian (many of which predated the more often mentioned European discoveries) and the propensity of people to gamble, it would seem logical that the mathematics of chance would have been one of the earliest branches of study developed. In reality, it wasn't until the seventeenth century that a rigorous mathematics of probability was developed by French mathematicians Pierre de Fermat and Blaise Pascal. What explanation might you give for this late development?

Featured Consultant for This Chapter

Richard Sgarlotti *is a longtime math teacher who is currently a consultant at the Hannahville Indian School in the Hannahville Potawatomi Community in Michigan. He works with staff and students on summer STEM projects and math curriculum development. Rich has worked with many American Indian organizations, especially in the area of integrating Native culture into the mathematics curriculum. He is the editor and major contributor to the volume* Creating a Sacred Place for Students in Mathematics, K–12, *published by the National Indian School Board Association.*

References

Barta, James, Marilyn Cuch, and Virginia Norris Exton. "When Numbers Dance for Mathematics Students: Culturally Responsive Mathematics Instruction for Native Youth." In *Voices of Native American Educators,* edited by Sheila T. Gregory, pp. 145–66. Lanham, Md.: Lexington Books, 2012.

Barta, Jim, Corinne Jetté, and Dawn Wiseman. "Dancing Numbers: Cultural, Cognitive, and Technical Instructional Perspectives on the Development of Native American Mathematical and Scientific Pedagogy." *Educational Technology Research and Development* 51, no. 2 (2003): 87–97.

Barta, Jim, and Tod Shockey. "The Mathematical Ways of an Aboriginal People: The Northern Ute." *Journal of Mathematics and Culture* 1, no. 1 (2006): 79–89.

Biggers, John. *Ananse: The Web of Life in Africa.* Austin: University of Texas Press, 1962.

Bishop, Alan. *Mathematical Enculturation: A Cultural Perspective on Mathematics Education.* Norwell, Mass: Kluwer Academic Publishers, 1988.

Boone, Sylvia Ardyn. *Radiance from the Waters: Ideals of Feminine Beauty in Mende Art.* New Haven, Conn.: Yale University Press, 1986.

D'Ambrosio, Ubiratan. "What Is Ethnomathematics, and How Can It Help Children in Schools?" *Teaching Children Mathematics* 7, no. 6 (2001): 308–10.

Gilroy, Paul. *The Black Atlantic: Modernity and Double Consciousness.* London, U.K.: Verso, 1993.

National Council of Teachers of Mathematics (NCTM). *Principles and Standards for School Mathematics.* Reston, Va.: NCTM, 2000.

National Governors Association Center for Best Practices and Council of Chief State School Officers (NGA Center and CCSSO). *Common Core State Standards for Mathematics.* Washington, D.C.: NGA Center and CCSSO, 2010. http://www.corestandards.org.

Rizenthaler, Robert. *The Potawatomi Indians of Wisconsin.* Milwaukee Public Museum Bulletin 19, no. 3 (1953).